C.D. Gibson R.T.

t. CARL ROSE C.D. Gibson F. Opper

GLUYAS WILLIAMS

Dave Breger

Whitney Darrow Jr. Robt Day

NALD MARSH Whitney Darrow Jr.

H. C. GREENING

T. S. Sullivant

RTON J. M. Flagg. McCUTCHEON

R. O. T. Minor Briggs "TAD" Sh

Boardman Robinson

J. R. WILLIAMS Don He

Perlman / Shellhase

Gardner Rea Jr SIDNEY SMITH

COVARRUBIAS ala

O. SOGLOW Thurber

Alan Dunn Wm Steig.

AN ROTH

REA IRVIN Dave Br

F. Fox ed Nofziger

chon Day alain

nan Peter Arno

CROCKETT JOHNSON

Shermund

BUNNY SWINNERTON

R. F. Outcault

Gibson

Breger GL W

REGINALD MARSH Whitney Da

MCMANUS

T. S. Sullivant

CARTOON CAVALCADE

EDITED BY

Thomas Craven

ASSISTED BY

Florence and Sydney Weiss

PEOPLES BOOK CLUB EDITION

Published by

CONSOLIDATED BOOK PUBLISHERS

CHICAGO

1945

ABOUT THE APPEARANCE OF BOOKS IN WARTIME

A recent ruling by the War Production Board has curtailed the use of paper by book publishers in 1943.

In line with this ruling and in order to conserve materials and manpower, we are co-operating by:

1. Using lighter-weight paper, which reduces the bulk of our books substantially.
2. Printing books with smaller margins and with more words to each page. Result: fewer pages per book.

Slimmer and smaller books will save paper and plate metal and labor. We are sure that readers will understand the publishers' desire to co-operate as fully as possible with the objectives of the War Production Board and our government.

This is a special edition published exclusively for members of the Peoples Book Club, P.O. Box 6570-A
Chicago, Ill.

MANUFACTURED IN THE UNITED STATES OF AMERICA

EDITOR'S NOTE

THE FIRST consideration, in selecting the illustrations for this book, as I have pointed out in the text, was that the drawing must be funny. But the task of bringing the pictures together was not funny. It was a long and complicated business involving both a sense of humor and that curious quality known as the artistic temperament. Deceased cartoonists were well satisfied with the illustrations in their name; but living cartoonists had their own ideas on what pictures best represented them in a volume dealing not only with the course of laughter but also with the causes of laughter through the passing years. For the solution of the endless difficulties of selection, procurement, and appeasement, I am indebted to Florence and Sydney Weiss. In the preparation of the text, I have been helped by the following books: *Middletown,* by Robert S. and Helen M. Lynd; *Only Yesterday* and *Since Yesterday,* by Frederick Lewis Allen; *The Pocket History of the United States,* by Allan Nevins and Henry Steele Commager; and *The Rise of American Civilization,* by Charles A. and Mary R. Beard. I am particularly indebted to William Murrell's *A History of American Graphic Humor,* the only work of its kind and a monumental contribution to Americana. Murrell's history, besides being invaluable for reference, has recalled to me the old artists and funny men whose cartoons were a part of my education.

T. C.

PUBLISHERS' NOTE

FIRST, and above all, the publishers wish to express their deepest thanks to all the artists who have created their book.

A special debt of gratitude, impossible to attempt to repay in a brief acknowledgment, is owed by the publishers to the editors of *The New Yorker*. Their co-operation and generosity made available the enormous percentage of *New Yorker* cartoons appearing in *Cartoon Cavalcade*, without which, of course, there would have been no book worthy of the name.

We are grateful to Mr. Berry Rockwell, Mr. Chester Weil of King Features Syndicate, Mr. Gurney Williams, Cartoon Editor of *Collier's* magazine, and Mr. Laurence Pollinger of London for similar co-operation, and to the George Matthew Adams Service and the staff of the New York Public Library for their invaluable help.

We are indebted to the following copyright owners for permission to reprint cartoons owned by them: Bell Syndicate, Chicago Tribune and New York News Syndicate, Cincinnati Times-Star, Collier's, George Delacorte of Dell Publications, Walt Disney Productions, Farrar & Rinehart, Inc., Harper & Brothers and Harper's Magazine, King Features Syndicate, Ledger Syndicate, Liberty, Robert M. McBride & Co., NEA Service, Inc., New Masses and The Masses, New York Herald Tribune, New York Journal-American, Press Publishing Co., Saturday Evening Post, Charles Scribner's Sons, The New York Sun and the New York Herald Company, and Punch of London.

We are grateful, too, to Miss Antonia Holding, Miss Rosalie Barrow, and Miss Sonia Bleeker for the intelligent execution of the myriads of details attendant upon publication.

CONTENTS

PART ONE

American Humor and the New Century

I HAVE ALWAYS thought that the Americans are the funniest people on earth: the writers, Josh Billings, Artemus Ward, Mark Twain, Eugene Field, Bill Nye, Finley Peter Dunne, Ring Lardner, H. L. Mencken, Will Rogers, and Fred Allen; the artists, Opper, Sullivant, "Zim," McCutcheon, Kemble, Powers, Art Young, "Tad," Steig, Arno, and George Price; and the cockeyed comedians, of vaudeville, screen, and radio. I have, of course, the natural prejudices of an American, and I do not wish to press the point too far nor to make invidious distinctions. But I cannot think of the Swedes as being funny, nor the Swiss, nor the Prussians; the Negroes certainly, but not the Egyptians; the French, at times, in a farcical way, but the Japs never. I once complained to a Russian friend that I had found no humor in the literature or art of his country, and he answered promptly that life in Russia was no laughing matter—which was a crusher. During the present war, however, the Russians have issued as internal propaganda the most effectual cartoons produced by any of the combatants. They portray the Germans as vermin and as despicable, drunken cows—the cow for some Moscovite reason carrying humorous connotations. The Russians laugh at the crazy symbols, and then, their blood warmed for action, go out and kill Germans.

The English? Ah, those English! "Even the angels," as Mark Twain pointed out, "speak with an English accent." But since we have joined hands with the British in two wars; since the abolition of distance by the airplane and the radio, and the popularity of American movies and books with all sorts and conditions of British people, our ways are becoming their ways, and the divergence in the two brands of humor grows less and less as time goes on. Indeed, on the authority of Mencken, it may be said that American speech is the dominating factor in the enrichment of what used to be a common language, and what may well be a common language again—but this time the angels will be speaking with an American accent.

The English have maintained an extraordinarily high level of achievement in black-and-white drawing, from Hogarth to Low, but most of their humorous artists do not give me a laugh. They may be humorists, all right, and great ones—that, I do not deny—but they are not of my training. I look at the work of Leech, Keene, Du Maurier, and Beerbohm, for example, with unqualified admiration and some amusement, but it does not fetch a laugh. Thackeray, a wretched draftsman, made funny drawings occasionally, and so did Cruikshank, an illustrator of genius, and Phil May was a scream.

In recent years, with the interchange of gags, jokes, comedians, and ministers of state, English black-and-white humor has found a more responsive audience in America, two men in particular, Bairnsfather and Bateman, having contributed nobly to international laughter. These two have exerted considerable influence on the funny men of America, and they are included in the book, not with any notion of claiming them for our own, but as worthy ambassadors of the belly laugh.

The difference between the English and the American temperament is illuminated with fine intelligence and great decency of spirit by John Steinbeck in his recent dispatches from the British Isles. As a brief sample, I quote from his conversation with two airmen, one English, the other American, both members of a bombing squadron which had just returned from a raid on Germany. There had been fighting in the air and he asked the two men how they had fared. "We knocked them about a bit," the Englishman replied. "We shot the hell out of them," the American said. And neither, Steinbeck added, had quite told the truth. The first was the product of traditional restraint; the second came from a background of picturesque overstatement. The bombers had not replied literally, but they had revealed fundamental characteristics of the humor of the two nations. American cartoonists, or the most forceful and funny of them, have always prided themselves on their marksmanship; they are straight shooters, and they do not knock things about a bit, they shoot the hell out of them — sacred cows, stuffed shirts, fourflushers, prohibition agents, phonies of every creed and kind, fads, new ideas, sex, and the President of the United States—if he happens to be a Democrat.

For the American springs from a unique and, in many respects, a fortunate background. He has less regard for the past and his ancestors than has any other inhabitant of the planet. He leaves the house in which he was born, conceals his grandparents, and lays down the law to his children, who, in turn, break it, as he broke the law of his fathers, and grow up as they please. The American is born and bred with no cultural memories in his heart. He is the child of a civilization in which things are built for service, to be scrapped and replaced by more efficient models when the day of their usefulness is over. As a consequence, he is the most irreverent of all God's children. Nothing is too sacred for him to attack, tear down, and rebuild. When he sees a NO TRESPASSING sign, he forthwith takes a short cut, trampling down the ungrown hay. When his noble-minded preceptors try to inject into him a measure of classical veneration, he laughs and screams, "Oh, yeah!" He coined the word "debunk" and made it the battle cry of a reckless school of writers and cartoonists. He is always inventing a vocabulary of wisecracks and ridicule: expressions that come and go, such as, *laugh that off, so what?, baloney, applesauce, no bananas, no spinach, no dice, no soup, no soap!* He is the maker, the victim, and the destroyer of new things and new ideas, succumbing to quack religions, fake panaceas, systems of gadget education and cathartics, while creating a new form of culture, a grand and enviable and pragmatic culture, a culture without antecedents.

To the Americans, as shrewd old Boss Murphy put it, everything is a nine days' wonder. The Americans are the original decriers, the habitual deflaters, the champion reputation busters of the world; and the very fact that a man has won and deserved his reputation is good and sufficient reason for taking him down. "It's a free country, ain't it?" Then let us all move on the same level. We have, of course, our moments of hysterical glorification and tribute paying in the good old three-ring style; we all turn out to the home-coming of some channel swimmer, golfer, or aviator who has successfully performed his stunt abroad; we throw a million telephone books into the streets and reward the returning acrobat, or chauffeur, with movie and radio contracts; and we sit humbly at the feet of indigent European lecturers, pay them handsomely for their monologues, and hearken to their words of wisdom —hearken for an hour, anyway. But this is ephemeral byplay. Ere long the humorists get in their licks. In prose and line, they let the hero have it, stripping him of all glamour and consigning him to the inescapable oblivion reserved for ex-celebrities.

Thus it has happened that in the growth of the American spirit, and its richest concomitant—a sense of humor—the quality of irreverence has played a conspicuous role. This quality had its professional origin in Mark Twain, and it has appeared in one form or another, and in varying degrees, in the subsequent practitioners of the art of comedy: in writers as diverse as Sinclair Lewis and James Thurber; in artists ranging from the rowdy gang attached to *Puck* and *Judge* in the late nineteenth century to the boys and girls of *The New Yorker,* who shrink at nothing. We find it in our best painters—in Tom Benton, for instance, who thumbs his nose at cheesecloth goddesses and classical heroics, and enlivens the walls of the State Capitol of Missouri with pictures of the James brothers in action, Frankie and Johnny, Huck Finn, political bosses, and other local phenomena. In the bulk of our humor, the strong local flavor is too much for European tastes, and it should be kept in mind that, generally speaking, the farther one goes from the source, the less pointed the joke. The Chinese do not see anything funny in *The Innocents Abroad,* nor do the French, for that matter; and to the British, the *Indoor Sports* of "Tad" are horrible examples of American vulgarity.

The indigenous quality of irreverence, from the savage onslaughts of our political cartoonists to the gentler satire of Helen Hokinson, presupposes a victim for its shafts. Somebody is always getting the worst of it; some timid soul must be the goat. Little Jeff has been unmercifully mauled for thirty-five years; Krazy Kat's only hope in life is a dornick behind the ear; Jiggs is browbeaten daily by his ugly spouse; Donald Duck unfailingly double-talks himself into a drubbing; and the capitalist has never been portrayed in any other form than as a monster of cupidity. The enjoyment of this type of humor depends on how your sympathies and prejudices are involved. Poor old William Jennings Bryan was held up to ridicule in a thousand cartoons, one of which, by Tom Powers, I shall never forget. His head was bald on top, but the hair was rank and tousled over the nape of the neck like a hen's nest, and in the nest a number of hatching eggs were visible—presidential eggs. The caricature was printed in every Republican paper in the land, and millions guffawed, but it was far from humorous to the Great Commoner and to those who believed in the free coinage of silver at the ratio of sixteen to one.

In my early childhood, when I read Bill Nye's comic *History of England* for the first time, I had no doubt that it was the funniest book ever written. It is still good, but not so side-splitting after Dunkirk and the deeds of the British Eighth Army. The book was illustrated by Goodes and Richards, who, obviously, had read the text. The illustrations were wonderful. I remember one of Queen Victoria in the act of running the Empire. She was glum and fat and fundamentally enormous, and she was squatting on something suggestive of the evacuation stools designed for babies. Under the picture was a line from Nye: "The Queen reigns all day long on a cold hard throne." I laughed myself sick, but the British did not laugh. They couldn't take Bill Nye's magnificent rhetorical kidding — it was low-down sacrilege. They could enjoy *Huckleberry Finn* because the respectability occasionally flouted was essentially American and therefore susceptible of humor. But the *Connecticut Yankee*! That gigantic fable was an insult to the chivalry of an ancient race! It all depends, I repeat, on where one stands.

Psychologically, the American habit of taking sides on all questions, of construing life in terms of good or bad, of right or wrong, has impelled our outstanding humorists to proceed from a pronounced moral bias. Against this bias, I have nothing to say. It has not always brought forth good fruit; but it has produced Mark Twain and Walt Disney; Ring Lardner and "Tad," and scores of odd and irrepressible comedians whom you will welcome again, as old friends, in the pages that follow. Mark Twain was universally beloved because he was on the right side—the side of humanity. When not relaxing his sense of humor in some meandering improvisation or convulsing tomfoolery, he leveled his incomparable powers of righteous indignation at shams and humbugs and sanctified crooks. And Lord, how he could hate! "Andrew Carnegie," he exclaimed, "that miserable child of sin! Goliath's wife would have used him as a clothespin to hang a shirtwaist on the line."

The profane spirit of America, as it assumed shape and dimension in the arts, is a comparatively recent development. It is possible to find scattered specimens of black-and-white humor antedating the Civil War, but I defy anyone accustomed to the high jinks of the modern school to laugh at those dreary, distorted, far-fetched efforts at raillery. The first manifestations of any graphic humor worthy of the name appeared in the scandals of the new *Police Gazette,* published in 1876; in the new *Puck* of the same year; in *Judge,* which stepped out in 1871, and in *Life,* founded in 1883. From these pioneering journals, one might glean some choice specimens of uncouth jesting, genuine to the core and still fragrant, and an equal number of nice, refined authentic pleasantries in the English manner—but this is no history of humor. It is enough to say that the volume of comic drawings mounted impressively as the century waned, and that production from 1900 to the present has been beyond any man's capacity for enjoyment. One might call it overproduction. That was my verdict as I tunneled through the stock pile of reproductions. The final selective test was based on the simple question, "Is the picture funny?" There will be disagreements—I think I have made that plain—but there will be enough to go around. One of the virtues of American revelry is its abundance. We have never had to ration our humor.

II

Culturally, the twentieth century suffered from the hangover of fabulous trumpery accumulated in the nineties, the gilded age. The pioneer and the planter, diverting their energies from the land to the rich industrialism of the mine and the factory, piled up mountains of wealth, and then gravitated, as the Beards have written, to the places where gorgeous objects could be had for money and displayed to gaping multitudes, the bravest of the socially ambitious horde migrating to the most powerful center of accumulation, New York City. "On their arrival in a metropolis, they advertised their vanity by erecting palaces, buying art, and giving social exhibitions. Along the streets and boulevards rose French châteaux, Italian mansions and English castles, with occasionally a noble monument to the derivative genius of some architect trained in Europe" — Stanford White, most likely, who designed the old Madison Square Garden, and whose polished lecheries were ended by a millionaire from Pittsburgh. Nothing to match the new American plutocracy had been seen since the decline of Rome. The "400" appeared, the closed circle of social aristocracy. The Goulds, Vanderbilts, Astors, and their kind, offspring of traders and buccaneers, enhanced their prestige by marrying into European nobility, to the disdain of the populace and the comic artists; and round the moneyed arbiters swarmed the sycophants and lackeys—shopkeepers, impoverished dukes, art dealers, fashionable European painters, and other beggars.

Outside the big cities, culture was more earnestly sought and more equitably diffused. Electric signs began to twinkle on Main Street, and domestic architecture was signally improved, the old General Grant Gothic yielding to a conglomerate style with spacious observation porches from which one could review the local bicycle club, a branch of the League of American Wheelmen, pedaling by in the dust. Bad taste was rampant, and the attempts to raise the standard, though praiseworthy, were more or less abortive. The new style of furniture, designated as mission or fumed oak, was dull and massive; houses were cluttered with sofa pillows fashioned from postal cards of burnt leather; and one encountered in every home the two inevitable eyesores, the Morris chair and the upright piano. The best-selling books of the first decade of the century followed two avenues of appeal: one the sentimental, as exemplified in *The Rose of Old St. Louis*, *Alice of Old Vincennes*, and *Three Weeks*, a daring piece of drivel imported from England to satisfy erotic curiosity, inasmuch as sex had not yet been recognized by Americans; the other, the call of the strenuous life as heeded in the red-blooded fictions of Jack London and Rex Beach. Browning Clubs composed of she-worshipers convened fortnightly to debate the ambiguities of the British apostle of holiness, and the Chautauqua developed into a powerful agency for mass refinement, enlisting the talents of active politicians, vagabond poets, chalk talkers, and washed-up spellbinders of the Bob Ingersoll school of oratory. Pictures were in great demand, for the most part, reproductions of magazine illustrators. There was a Gibson Girl in every dormitory; and from coast to coast—in the homes of Boston bankers and Ohio glass manufacturers, in the Texas ranch house and the floorless cabin of the Southern hillbilly—the prints of Maxfield Parrish shone out in prophylactic splendor. Parrish was not only the most popular artist of those pre-World War days, he remains the most popular artist begotten in America. The pin-up girl of thirty years ago was *September Morn*, a French bathing beauty whose chaste, averted nudity was denounced by Anthony Comstock of the Society for the Suppression of Vice. The ensuing publicity was nation-wide and more than a million copies of the print were sold.

With the expansion of practical science came material comforts and mechanized pleasures. The bathroom was no longer a luxury, but the beauty parlor was unknown and the use of cosmetics was the prerogative of the oldest profession. Girls guarded their femininity in those days and left the coarser pleasures of drinking and smoking to the men. A girl might use the telephone for business purposes, but it was not meet for her to call a boy friend. The telephone had become a necessity; it hung on the wall and it had to be cranked, but it worked. Gas and electricity were within the reach of most householders; Edison's new-fangled machine on the parlor table played *The Georgia Camp Meeting* — but the radio was unborn. At the Bijou Theater on the corner, a new and unadulterated American art, the movie, was showing a Keystone Comedy, with Charlie Chaplin, Fatty Arbuckle, and the lovely Mabel Normand.

The horseless carriage had evolved into the automobile, and Henry Ford was tinkering with a new type of internal-combustion motor he had seen at the St. Louis Fair. The Wright brothers, dismissed by the financiers of Dayton as a couple of crackpots, had concluded their experiments at Kitty Hawk, and the flying machine was transformed into the airplane. Glenn Martin was attending the high school at Salina, Kansas, but without illustrious results. He was a classmate of mine, and I can depose that while his spelling was poor and his grammar in need of repairs, he was an adept at wisecracking and irreverence. His extracurricular successes were more notable. He was a duck shooter of parts and a master of guns and machines. Eventually he "accepted a position"—that's the way respectable boys got jobs in those days—in the town's first garage—and soon threw the whole country into a panic by driving a no-good car at the unexampled speed of forty miles an hour. The printed version of the story was that young Martin, unable to shut off the motor, had driven wildly up and down and across cow pastures and wheat fields, chasing the livestock and scaring the farmers out of their wits. The truth was that he was merely indulging his sense of humor; but the short-grass cartoonists of the Middle West fell greedily on the episode and made the most of it in a series of strips recounting the daily progress and amazing adventures of a runaway automobile piloted by a green country boy. The joke had endless possibilities, and at this late day, cartoonists are wont to rework it. One fine autumn, at the wheel of a better car, young Martin headed straight for the West Coast and arrived at Santa Monica without once stopping the engine—so he said. A few years afterward, he appeared again in Salina, but this time as a barnstorming aviator in a plane of his own design and construction. With his old flair for dressiness, he had arrayed his tall frame in a uniform that was black from helmet to boots. He looked like a celestial undertaker.

In those days a boy could go places. He could go faster and farther, save in the Solid South, if he voted the Republican ticket, and refrained from being queer. The unstable tenets of psychoanalysis had not been formulated, and nobody worried about inhibitions or frustrations. Nor was there any such thing as the inferiority complex—not after Grover Cleveland had told the British where to get off in Venezuela. Our high-brow artists looked to Europe for salvation, as they had always done —but had no public; our purveyors of comedy, contented and well paid, looked on America as the promised land—their public was enormous and ever-increasing. Gifted, uninhibited young men, more often than not, self-taught, migrated from the sticks and smaller cities to New York, the market place of the nation. From San Francisco came Homer Davenport, the political cartoonist, and Rube Goldberg, Jimmy Swinnerton, "Tad" (Thomas A. Dorgan), George Herriman, and Bud Fisher, among the first and best of the comic strippers.

In the latter part of the nineteenth century, Thomas Nast, of *Harper's Weekly*, had developed the black-and-white drawing into a terrible instrument of destruction. Nast, however, was not a humorist. In the opening years of the twentieth century, when the daily political cartoon became an established force in the editorial policy of metropolitan newspapers—and perhaps the most potent force—our enterprising young artists sought to devise a new type of political weapon combining the power and technique of Thomas Nast with their own particular brands of humor, but only a few succeeded. The conspicuous successes were Homer Davenport and F Opper, in New York, and three men from Chicago, John T. McCutcheon, Art Young, and T. E. Powers.

Homer Davenport was an odd compound of raw native wit and intellectual penetration of a rare order. His talents ripened in the free air sweeping the Golden Gate, and he came East at the invitation of Hearst, as the advertised successor of Nast. That he lived up to the title is not a matter of controversy. His caricatures of Platt, Hanna, McKinley, Bryan, the pink-whiskered Ham Lewis, and the Rough Rider are the ranking masterpieces of the rogues' gallery of American art. Davenport was a plain-speaking man with a charming simplicity, not to say homeliness, of manner, but he affected a casualness and innocence which disguised a gorgeous vein of practicality. He was about as dumb as Will Rogers often professed to be. Commissioned to execute a series of caricatures of British statesmen, he went to England, where the story of his bout with Gladstone was repeated in the clubs of London. I offer the incident as I heard it from the late W. E. Lewis, editor of the old *Morning Telegraph* and one of Davenport's cronies.

"I had quite a tussle with the old opium trader," Davenport said. "I went down to his farm, by appointment, but when I reached the place, they told me the Right Honorable was not to home—they said he was out somewhere in the forest chopping wood. They didn't offer me no assistance, but I finally located him sitting on a stump looking very mournful and holding an ax in his hand. There was a flock of big crows flying round the house and through the trees and so I begun again to make conversation.

" 'You've got the finest crows here, Mr. Gladstone, that I ever seen, and I've seen 'em everywhere.' That fixed him.

" 'Them ain't crows!' he shouted in the biggest voice I ever heard. 'Them ain't crows, them's rooks!'

"He started to warm up a little and got right friendly, and asked me how much I charged for a picture. I told him I usually got five hundred bucks.

" 'I don't know how much five hundred bucks might be in English money,' he said, 'but it must be a hell of a lot of dough in any language. Couldn't you go easy on me, and come down a bit, me being a Prime Minister and you being only an American?'

" 'Sure,' I said, 'I'll meet you halfway. I'll do it for one hundred bucks—but it will look just like you.'

"He didn't crack a smile, but I could see that he was interested, and so I chopped a cord of wood for him, and then got down to work and made the drawing. It didn't take long, but when he peered at it, he put up an awful howl—and I knowed it looked just like him. After he had quit cussing me, he begged me not to show the drawing to no one—said it would ruin his career. I promised him I wouldn't, and being a man of my word, I kept my promise. At least, I kept it for a day or so."

The most fecund and popular of the newspaper cartoonists of the new century was Frederick Burr Opper. To a generation conditioned by the facile spoofing of *The New Yorker*, Opper has limited appeal, but with due allowance for shifting tastes and standards, it may be said that he is assured of the place of honor in the outhouse of American art.

After twenty-five years of uproarious productivity for *Puck*, Opper signed up with Hearst, for whom he worked thirty-two years more, not only as fabricator of comic strips but also as political cartoonist number one, an unparalleled record of continuous service. Poor vision terminated his career in 1932. "I could no longer see the point of my cartoons," he said, with a laugh on the wrong side of his mouth, "and I had to quit." His purpose was not to present human beings but to create ludicrous effigies of brutalized power and venality, his Willie (McKinley), Teddy (Roosevelt), and Nursie (Mark Hanna), for example, in his most famous published work, *Willie and His Poppa*. In this and in his other collections, he personified The Trusts as a Gargantuan bully, a grinning predatory creature that oppressed a little, defenseless puppet called The Common People. Opper's influence on political artists and comic strippers may be observed in the multitude of contemporary practitioners, but most of them are pallid and humorless by the side of the master.

T. E. Powers, another Hearst protégé, could hardly be called an artist of studio refinements, but unlike Opper, he was neither raucous nor grossly abusive in his political sorties. His cartoons looked like the easiest things in the world to design—until his imitators tried it; and his capricious humor they could not steal without immediate detection.

Few cartoonists have won more esteem and affection from their colleagues, and few have afforded more real enjoyment to the public, than Art Young, of Chicago and the U. S. A. He was born with a sense of humor which he has expressed in an extremely concise and robust fashion—a truly Falstaffian humor that seldom misses fire, whether it be directed at social evils or at the foibles of the passing show. In his early period, he was employed by a Chicago newspaper, and during those years published his *Hades Up to Date,* a work labeled old-fashioned, of late; but if you cannot laugh over the drawings of that book, then, I must insist, your sense of humor is pretty thin and meager. In New York he made pictures for the old *Life* and other journals, his humor dealing satirically, but none the less sympathetically, with the homely and often laughable habits of plain Americans, the simple, the childish, and the aged.

Many of Art Young's drawings appeared in *The Masses,* a Socialist magazine, with John Sloan as art editor and a brilliant group of contributors. *The Masses* called into service a brilliant group of contributors, among them, George Bellows, Boardman Robinson, William Glackens, Glen Coleman, Robert Minor, H. W. Glintenkamp, at that time the most distinguished draftsmen in America. These men were propagandists and reformers, and humor was incidental to the social message.

The first cartoonists to come within my experience were the rollicking crew employed by *Puck,* and John T. McCutcheon, the bright particular star of the *Chicago Record-Herald.* When I was a boy in the Dust Bowl, my father subscribed to both papers in order that my education in American humor might not be neglected.

You did not have to agree with McCutcheon's political views to enjoy his drawings. He was not a powerful artist and his political convictions sat rather lightly upon him, but his humor was irresistible. It was a gentle form of humor, perennially fresh and blithe, and saturated with the milk of human kindness. When he depicted Hinky Dink and Bathhouse John, Chicago's most notorious wardheelers, he made them over into an engaging pair of scalawags; and when, in his *Bird Center* extravaganzas, he satirized the pretensions of culture-seeking Americans, he was neither harsh nor offensive. He was on intimate terms with the restless, self-conscious Middle Westerners, and their embarrassing social aspirations elicited his humorous indulgence, never his condemnation. McCutcheon lavished all his warmth and understanding on the American boy's rebellion against artificial respectability, and his celebrated *Boy in Springtime* drawings have dated little with the march of time.

Two artists who held their public from the old century into the new were E. W. Kemble and A. B. Frost. The first had illustrated *Huckleberry Finn,* and no more harmonious accord between text and pictures could be imagined. Mark Twain had no faith in the power of the written word to convey the physical attributes of a character, and for that reason never bored his readers with itemized descriptions of faces and figures. "No two people agree on the looks of a character," he said, "so why try the reader's patience?" When he beheld Kemble's conceptions in black and white, he chuckled with approval. "Perfect!" he exclaimed. "My dear immaculate family as I created them!" Which, to the artist, was praise from the Lord. Kemble, though not a Southerner, had a sharp perception of the Negro's lot in the world, and of the resilient humor which lifted the black man's spirits in long, hard times. Year after year, with unfailing gusto, he delighted his public with boisterously funny presentations of the Negro, some of which were collected from *Life* and published in an album called *Comical Coons.* Kemble's pen line was loose and shaggy, but he used it with remarkable expressiveness in the drawing of faces and in humanizing his charades of wild life, with lions, bears, and snakes as the actors.

A. B. Frost, after his definitive illustrations for *Uncle Remus,* veered into political cartooning, but with scarcely creditable results. Returning to his unforced talent he became a fixture with *Life,* entertaining an eager set of readers with his droll, bucolic fancies. Frost's drolleries, at best, were only a mild stimulant to the glands of humor, and his rustics are models of propriety to those who enjoy the rancid humor of the modern hillbilly cartoonists—but his illustrations for *Uncle Remus* are genuine Americana.

The animal humorist par excellence of the overlapping period was T. S. Sullivant. He first appeared in 1888, in the infancy of *Life,* and connoisseurs of laughter sat up and took notice. His debut was a drawing of *A High-Bred Man on a Low-Bred Horse,* a monocled ass sprawling on a cylindrical prism, funny then and funny now, but the soul of academic decorum compared with his mature performances. Sullivant had a curious imagination and a unique method of expressing it. He created with convincing realism and solidity a menagerie of forms which any other artist would have made fantastic and humorless. His lumbering faunas have a prehistoric bulk, but there is something sly and contemporary in all of them. As Homer Davenport said, "They don't look made up. They look like they growed that way."

During this period, Harrison Cady, who survives in his current strip, *Peter Rabbit,* filled whole pages of *Life* with the microscopic enterprises of Bugville and Beetleburg; and Walt Kuhn, now a modernist painter, of all things, made charming little sketches of misbehaving animals, and naughty birds peering into ladies' bathhouses. Eugene Zimmerman—"Zim" to all lovers of humor—technically, a relative of Opper and as native as red liquor, was the spokesman of the humbler social orders whom he treated, not as inferiors nor as the underprivileged, but as self-sufficient Americans out of luck but very friendly and capable of laughter. A more sensitive observer, with a black-and-white style acquired in Paris and Munich, was Michael Angelo Woolf, who died in 1899, bequeathing to the new century a body of drawings of fine tenderness and distinction.

The cosmopolitan cartoonist was Hy Mayer, celebrated in London, Paris, and Berlin, contributor to *Figaro* and *Jugend,* and, from 1904 to 1914, attached to *The New York Times,* where his *Impressions of the Passing Show* were set down with astonishing agility and a fanciful humor that has not altogether faded. The whimsical favorite was Peter Newell, illustrator of Bangs' *A Houseboat on the Styx,* whose quaint style and odd, imaginative twists endeared him to an audience of all ages. Oliver Herford was the literary humorist, that is to say, his drawings were most effective when supplemented by a text. His sharp satires in line, and his parodies of the styles of other artists, were enjoyed by a limited but ardent public. J. Conacher, who could draw anything well and sometimes with humor, deserves a reminiscent word of praise, together with Frank A. Nankivell, a man of full-dress elegance in style and subject matter, and a rare bird in *Puck's* stable of low comedians. But in popular fame, none of these worthy gentlemen could hold a candle to Charles Dana Gibson.

The glory that was Gibson has gone into history. To appreciate the magnitude of the man's fame and influence, one must have lived in the generation whose ideals and humors he expressed with relentless brilliancy. Other artists have exceeded him in certain elements of popularity: Maxfield Parrish, in the sales of his prints; any number of syndicated merchants of the comic strip in the size of their public; and Walt Disney, working in a medium which releases his animations simultaneously to millions. But no other artist has exerted so great an influence on the politer trends of social conduct, and none has incarnated an ideal of young womanhood so acceptable to the American people.

Gibson was born in Massachusetts in 1867, attended the public schools at Flushing, Long Island, disclosed in childhood exceptional dexterity in paper cutouts, and enrolled in the Art Students' League, of New York, at the age of seventeen. The following year he timorously left a batch of drawings with John Ames Mitchell, founder and editor of *Life.* One of the drawings was purchased for the sum of four dollars, and the boy was a professional artist. Three years later, Mitchell wrote: "No American artist now before the public is the happy possessor of so many desirable qualities as Mr. Charles Dana Gibson, and of these the rarest, and not the least important, is his ability to draw a lady."

Gibson, then only a beginner, had already asserted the inimitable quality which was to make him, or his Girl, the American idol. But before settling down to the business of glorifying young womanhood, he had a few humorous wild oats to sow. He sowed them in good rich ground, and when the harvest came, it contained perhaps the most thoroughly humorous drawings he ever signed. One, from the year 1888, was called *Erin's Dream,* a representation of an Irish Triumph, with Old Queen Victoria riding backward on a donkey, a sodden Harp reclining on a float, strolling pigs and geese, and John Bull hanging in effigy—a regular shanty Irish picnic and a piece of irreverence worthy of Opper. Another, done somewhat later when he was edging toward the upper crust, was entitled *The Salons of New York*—a glimpse of a high-class affair in which the town's elite comport themselves with the abandon of barroom drunks.

The Gibson Girl was received with the fine, uncritical frenzy which Americans bestow upon objects of justifiable emulation. She had health and beauty, strength and dignity, and the aloofness inherent in an ideal. She was approved by the "400"; shopgirls and coeds modeled their clothes and their deportment, and shaped their bodies, after her image; and Gibson, with a crafty stroke, made her the commander of men, the herald of the emancipated woman—a fact not unpleasing to the rising species. She had everything save sex appeal and humor: the first was forbidden, the second inconsistent with divinity. Worshiped at home, she was admired abroad, and in the heyday of her dominion, her stately presence was global. According to one chronicler, "Gibson albums were found in the palace of the last Czar, after his exile, and sketches of the Girl decorated palm-leaf huts in Central America, cabins in the Klondike and Australia, Tokyo shopwindows, and the cabooses of freight trains."

Gibson kept the Girl alive beyond the span normally allotted to deities by his indefatigable tenacity and by introducing her, together with the rest of the family, to the fashionable world of the European capitals. And for the sake of this book, let it be noted that his sense of humor did not desert him. The Girl was too lofty to be treated lightly, but in the drawings called *The Weaker Sex,* where the square-jawed male pursuer is reduced to fatuous servility, there is a saving humor, of sorts. And in other drawings of the last period, *The Champ* and *Two Strikes and the Bases Full,* for example, the situation is intrinsically funny and the rendering robust and jovial.

While Gibson was devoting his energies—and he was a horse for work—to the cultural predicaments of American High Life, men of another breed were busy with an art form, or a fun form, which was soon to become a national industry. These men had no mission, no message, no ideals: the sole excuse for their existence was to compel laughter. They knew little about culture and cared less, yet they were a definite product of a native cultural tendency, the unpolluted tradition that inspired the humor of Mark Twain—two, in fact, having illustrated Mark Twain. The first successful exhibit of the new fun form appeared in the Sunday supplement of the New York *World,* November 18, 1894, a momentous date in the history of humor. The exhibit was R. F. Outcault's colored sequence unfolding in six boxes the singular transformation of an anaconda after it had swallowed a succulent yellow dog. The sequence was entitled *The Origin of a New Species,* a prophetic caption, for it announced the birth of a new species of entertainment, the comic strip in color.

The vogue of the colored continuity, to borrow a term from the movies, began three years later with Outcault's *Hogan's Alley,* in which the interest was centered upon a single character, a lop-eared, one-toothed ragamuffin from the tenements; and when the ragamuffin, by a printer's vagary, was brightened up like an acre of sunflowers and inducted into a new saga called *The Yellow Kid,* the comic strip was on the way to the supercolossal, and sometimes detestable, popularity it enjoys at the present time. The continuous episode had been used by artists like Bellew and Haworth in the eighties; but the honor of adding color and of presenting the same characters day after day, decade after decade, must be conferred on Outcault. It is not stretching the truth too far to say that the comic strip, in its present form, began with *The Yellow Kid.*

Whereupon, there was hot rivalry among the newspapers, and artists were bought and sold like baseball players. Outcault was bought by Hearst, for whom he fathered *The Yellow Kid,* but the *World* retained the copyright to

Hogan's Alley and continued the older strip as a parallel attraction, the drawing and coloring done to order by George Luks, the painter. The two Kids vied with each other for popular support, and it is possible, as someone has suggested, that out of the gaudy competition came the term "yellow journalism"—but on that point of color and ethics I am no authority. Rudy Dirks, author of the original *Katzenjammer Kids,* also joined the Hearst forces, but at the cost of the title of his strip, the copyright of which was held by the *World.* An excellent painter and a man of extraordinary inventiveness, Dirks immediately instituted an equivalent and more exciting attraction, *The Captain and the Kids,* a low-bred fantasia of unlessened popularity, notwithstanding the odium attached to things Teutonic. As the comic industry increased in public appeal, and hence in wealth, the artists began to drive hard bargains and to copyright strips in their own names, thereby protecting their share in the royalties derived from the syndicates, and also multiplying their incomes into figures hardly surpassed in the tax returns of the wage earners of Hollywood.

In the first period of the new form of comedy, the staple of many artists was immigrant or racial humor, and for two reasons. First, the strutting self-confidence and nationalism disseminated by Theodore Roosevelt; second, the unrestricted immigration which gave the United States the name of Melting Pot, and which localized throughout the nation whole communities of "foreigners" whose unfamiliar customs were meat and drink to our ribald jokesters. The stage comedians were caricatures of foreigners and unassimilated Americans: Germans played by Weber and Fields, Dockstader's Negro minstrels, French sissies, Irish braggarts, and the obtuse Englishman—always the silly ass of the troupe. I recall without pride the performance of a band of barnstorming comedians who came to my home town when I was in knee pants. Of the three principals, two impersonated Swedes of the type commonly known as squarehead, and the third was a German goof. The point of the show, if any, was to arouse laughter by playing on the imbecilities of foreigners; and every now and then, a gag was repeated like a bawling refrain: "It takes two dumb Swedes to make one dumb German"—at which everybody roared. The existence near by of a settlement of Swedes who maintained a school of painting and a chorus of six hundred voices for the annual festival at Easter could not dispel the superstition that the Swede was a witless squarehead, the *Yens Yenson* of the comic supplement.

The comic strip reflected the popular attitude of the day, not with malice, but with profound irreverence and telling laughter. The Irish caught it in George McManus' *Jiggs* and Opper's *Happy Hooligan,* the Negro in Kemble's *Black Berries,* the Germans in the two strips by Dirks, the French in Opper's *Alphonse and Gaston,* the Jew in Harry Hershfield's *Abie the Agent.* The old familiar faces are gone now, all but the mugs of Jiggs and Maggie, and the Captain's scowl, and the artist has no more need of immigrant or racial humor. It should be noted, in this connection, that the comic strip was not originally designed for children. The kids loved it from the beginning, but the grownups loved it more. It became the exclusive property of the young—often children of arrested development—when the comedy went out, and the mystery came in, a curious by-product which we shall look into at the proper time.

The first daily strip appeared in the *San Francisco Chronicle,* in 1907, signed and also copyrighted by Bud Fisher. It was a running account of the machinations of *A. Mutt,* a race-track tout with an engaging indifference to honest toil. Two years later, the tall imposter struck an alliance with *Little Jeff,* and these twin oddities, timeless and unregenerate, are the oldest extant characters in the funny pages of the press. They have no counterparts in the real world; they never do anything decent or edifying, they have all the instincts of knaves and none of the talent—yet they are more widely known than Sherlock Holmes, and have almost as many followers as Mickey Mouse. I follow them religiously, but to some of my friends they give only a headache. Whatever else the two rogues may be, they are characters, perhaps the most completely realized individuals in the crowded world of native comedy. They run true to form, and hold their public not by any single act of low-lived audacity, but by the constant pressure of their humorous personalities. In this they resemble Charlie Chaplin, or the Chaplin of the old days, before he was burdened with a social message.

Of somewhat earlier vintage was *Nervy Nat,* drawn for the weekly *Judge* by James Montgomery Flagg, and drawn with exceptional cleverness. Flagg has been before the public for forty-five years or more, as book and magazine illustrator and humorist in line, but his best work in the vein of comedy was done at the beginning of the century. In *Nervy Nat,* he depicted in sequence the adventures of an American bum in Paris, where he was nearly beaten to death for his impudence, and afterward, in many parts of the homeland where he was treated with the contempt generally accorded to bums. The gaiety of the period was reflected in *Fluffy Ruffles,* a series of drawings by Wallace Morgan with verses by Carolyn Wells. The humor of *Fluffy Ruffles* is almost imperceptible today, but the freshness and skill of the drawings have not been impaired by time.

George Herriman's *Krazy Kat,* a product of the sunshine of California, has endured since 1911; a delight saddened by Herriman's death in 1944. The plaintive humor of this miniature drama with its foregone conclusion cannot be grasped in a single strip; one must know and love the silly Kat, the calculating Ignatz Mouse, and the Pup—the flat-foot of the law—to enjoy the original flavor of the successive episodes. There is more in the apparently aimless repetitions than at first meets the eye of one jaded with the violent action of run-of-the-mill adventures. The dialogue, a hotchpot of quaint puns and Mexican patois, and the landscapes artfully contrived of stage settings in a desert, are pleasurable in themselves, but the humor lies in the enforcement of the moral law that the rewards of sentimentality are harsh and crude. The humor is driven home with a brickbat, and Krazy Kat, yowling in vain for undeserved affection, gets what is coming to him, and to all sentimentalists. It seems more than probable that Walt Disney looked long and fondly at Ignatz Mouse before creating the insuperable Mickey, but that is nothing to worry about—there are no priorities in the comic strip.

Rube Goldberg studied engineering and mechanical drawing on the West Coast, rose to the rank of sports cartoonist, and, going higher and farther, won a luxurious spot for himself on the comic page. For a score of years he incited millions to laughter, rip-roaring laughter that pulled the midriff and made no sense. His *Foolish Questions, Phony Films,* and famous *Inventions* in which he complicated the performance of the simplest act by a screwball apparatus, burlesquing the machine age and the wasted energy of the poor boobs who accumulate so much baggage for so short a journey—these things have done more to set the world straight than his recent political cartoons.

For irreverence that is deadly and low hard-boiled humor, Thomas A. Dorgan, the one and only "Tad," stands apart from the artists of the comic strip as an indisputable master. Tad came to New York in 1905 to work for the sports department of the *Evening Journal* as cartoonist and occasional reporter. His oral jokes and punishing remarks in slang of original coinage found their way into his drawings, and soon he abandoned the sports cartoon for the strip, where his genius for splenetic humor ran riot, making the name of Tad a household word in America.

His *Indoor Sports* and *Outdoor Sports,* many of which have been reprinted of late, have lost none of their raffish comedy. They are good for a long time, I think—as long as society carries a surplus of shysters and spongers. The culprits he selected were viciously caricatured and funny enough as they stood, but the full, complete, and soul-satisfying humor was in the combination of the drawing and the verbal comments—the title, the dialogue, and the tiny figure in the corner springing a gag, an intentionally corny rhyme, or some exhortation such as "Quick Watson, the needle!"

Tad coined and gave currency to slang expressions which are still used by the masses, by purists and humorists, and by members of Congress. In looking over strips drawn twenty-five or thirty years ago, I find these captions: *Piping a Tank Town Wise Cracker As He Does His Stuff in a Big Town Dept. Store, Listening to an Egg Who Is Trying to Talk His Storm Out of a New Layout, Talking with and About the Iron Man Who Delivers the Mail—Most of Which Is Just Bologne;* and the gags, *Yes We Have No Bananas, What, No Spinach!,* and *Applesauce!*

Tad had a sense of justice as well as a sense of humor. Take his *Silk Hat Harry's Divorce Suit,* for example, the high point of his genius, a strip in which the characters are a pack of yahoos—dogs possessing all the cheats and snide instincts of human beings, and none of the graces. You may laugh your head off as you gaze and read, but you need waste no sympathy on the scurvy, double-crossing dogs. Tad was popular because his humor was intelligently directed.

Tad had no illusions about himself or his public. "My stuff is for the gents," he said. "The squaws don't get me." He lived long enough to see the hard-boiled, gin-drinking girls of the twenties raving over his strips, and to hear the intellectuals discussing his humor in the balderdash of aesthetics. His disgust hastened his death. In his last years, illness confined him to the seclusion of one room and he passed the time at the radio, "listening to the phony announcers," he said, "and the hams faking their stories of the prize fights."

A SLIPPERY DAY

"Guess if I'm careful I'll get along." "By Jove! it is slippery." "Oh, hang these slanting pavements!" "A man does have to have command of his feet on these bad spots."

"Steady does it!" "Oh dear me! I hope no one is looking!" "Now which way is he coming, anyhow?" "Excuse me!" "I beg your pardon!"

"Happy thought! What's the use of walking." "— — — — —!" "It's a mighty hard winter, anyhow." "If ever I go out on a day like this again—"

The Fatal Mistake

A Tale of a Cat

A FEW THINGS THE VERSATILE YELLOW KID MIGHT DO FOR A LIVING

"If I gits married I got ter hustle if I wants ter keep de wolf away furninst me door."

"I'm stuck on der perleece, an' I tink I could do it, 'cause bein' a cop is dead easy."

"Composin' music dese days is easy; all yer have ter do is ter buy Gilbert and Sullivan and de 'Chimes of Normandy' an' yez kin rite an opera."

"I might earn some money on Park Row by shakin' de bones."

"I tink I could give parlor entertainments fer de '400' or play fer de Patriarchs' ball."

"If some pretty girl wot has got a good altogether will pose fer me I'll paint a nood. I'll ask ballet girl; she's a peach."

"It costs too much to be a real sport an' win prizes at de horse show"—

—"but I tink I would be a good jockey an' a prize winner fer some one else."

"If I could jist git in ter de fish business I could make money an' live on me stock."

"Dis is one ting I wouldn't do; I would much radder work."

Wall Street's New Guardian

Who Trusts Trusts Is Sure to Be Robbed.—*Proverbs of the 19th Century*

Uncle Sam (from behind the door) : "Drop Them 'ere Pants!"

N. B.—He'll be lucky if they don't keep his "pants."

"Has father got here yet?"

"THE COURSE OF TRUE LOVE," etc. HE: *"There's the only girl I ever loved, an' I dassent go near her 'cause she's gittin' the measles."*

"If yer please, mum, Santa Claus can't get into our room 'cause they ain't no chimley, an' I want ter know if yer won't hang up this stockin' when yer a-hangin' up the children's, an' I'll call in the mornin' fer it."

THE FIRST NEW ENGLAND PIE

"Forsooth, your Excellency, she must be a witch; else how hath she put in the contents without breaking the crust?"

"IT'S RUN DOWN. I'LL GET OUT THE AUXILIARY MOTOR."

"COME ALONG, JENNY!"

"IT MAY BE SLOW, BUT WE'LL GET HOME."

Tale of Spooney Island

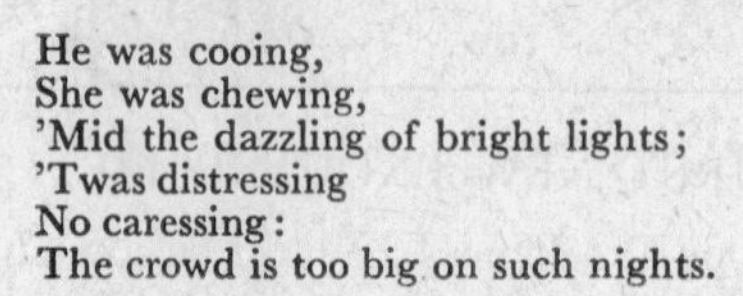

He was cooing,
She was chewing,
'Mid the dazzling of bright lights;
'Twas distressing
No caressing:
The crowd is too big on such nights.

No second missing
With hugging, kissing,
Their loss was made up in the dark.
The Gods had mercy
With poor Percy:
The lights died out and left no sparks.

Alas! their kissing,
By electric hissing,
Was suddenly turned into glum:

Like clouds in thunder,
They broke asunder,
Tied but by a string of chewing gum.

"If Willie is a good boy, and minds Papa and Nursie, they will try to let him keep the pretty house until he is eight years old."

"What ails you, Willie?"
"Look at that campaign banner that Teddy has painted!"

"Yes, Willie, this is a rubber toy to amuse you and Teddy. It represents the Working Classes. See how Papa pulls its leg."

"Yes, Willie, Papa's saddle horse is very cantankerous lately. I'm afraid he won't let Papa ride him much longer."

THE GREATEST GAME IN THE WORLD—*HIS MOVE*

WHEN DOCTORS DISAGREE

THE
ETERNAL
QUESTION

WIRELESS TELEGRAPHY

LAW ENFORCEMENT AT WHISKEY GULCH

"What are they moving the church for?"

"Well, stranger, I'm mayor of these diggin's, an' I'm fer law enforcement. We've got an ordinance what says no saloon shall be nearer than 300 feet from a church. I gave 'em three days to move the church."

THE WEAKER SEX—He takes a hand at bridge and has difficulty in keeping his mind on the game, with the result that he repeatedly trumps his partner's tricks.

"JILTED"

A Realistic Romance of Perils, Privations and Plunder

"Three shots for a nickel!"

These terrifying words were uttered by Pitiless Pierpont, the Scourge of the Spanish Main, as he stood on the deck of his low, black, rakish craft, *Grab*. His crew of crime-saturated freebooters were amusing themselves by throwing belaying pins, binnacle lamps and other hardware at their trembling captive. They were indeed tough citizens. When it came to assorted villainy they held the world's record.

Their terror-stricken prisoner gazed around him hopelessly.

"I'm it!" he muttered, in a despairing tone.

Powers' Presidential Possibilities—Republican

He thinks that Rockefeller would be appropriate, and outlines the probable Rockefeller cabinet as follows:

J. D. Rockefeller—President.

J. D. Rockefeller, Jr.—Secretary of the Treasury or High Custodian of the Key.

William Rockefeller (Bill)—Director of the Mints, to see that no one outside the family gets any money.

Stillman—General Suppressor of the Currency.

Aldrich—Attorney-General and Handy Man Around the Oil Tanks.

Foxy Grandpa Platt—Postmaster-General.

John W. Gates—Secretary of War, assisted by Chauncey Depew, Messenger.

Andy Carnegie—Secretary of the Golf Links.

Happy Hooligan Takes His Nephews to the Trained Dog Show.

POLICE
HELP
G-R-R
BOW WOW
OUCH
PROF RONZO'S DOG CIRCUS
POOR UNCLE HAPPY
SWAT HIM
PROF RONZO'S DOG CIRCUS
DON'T HIT UNCLE HAPPY
SHOT HIM
CLUB HIM
LEMME AT HIM
KEEP BACK
PROF RONZO'S DOG CIRCUS
UNCLE HAPPY'S PINCHED
GUILTY
WHAT IS YOUR VERDICT!
F Opper
CRIMINAL RECORD OF HAPPY HOOLIGAN VOL. 1
EVIDENCE AGAINST HOOLIGAN
PROF RONZO'S DOG CIRCUS
PEOPLE VS HOOLIGAN
EXHIBIT A

ALPHONSE, GASTON AND THEIR FRIEND LEON MEET BY CHANCE

THE IDEA!

Gymnasium Instructor—"Now, young ladies, all take a very deep breath, please. That's not half deep enough. Think of your favorite matinée idol, please. Ah, that's the idea. Now, exhale very slowly."

"That is certainly a queer place for a cherry to grow!"

Mr. Turtle: GEE! I'LL HAVE TO GIVE IT UP. EVERY TIME I TRY TO KISS HER SHE DRAWS IN HER HEAD.

THE NEWLYWEDS—Hubby Writes Her a Love Poem Out of His Own Head

THE NEWLYWEDS—Hubby's First Day of Vacation

BUSY LITTLE BUSTER BROWN

BUSY LITTLE BUSTER BROWN (*Continued*)

BUSTER BROWN GOES SHOOTING

BUSTER BROWN GOES SHOOTING (*Continued*)

THE KATZENJAMMER KIDS TAKE A PHOTOGRAPH BY FLASHLIGHT

FOXY GRANDPA

The Boys Were in a Very Mischievous Mood, But Grandpa Soon Cured Them

BOYS: "Let's warm up this seat for Gran'pa with a few of these little tacks."

GRANDPA: "I'll just lay a trap for those young mischiefs."

BOYS: "Hello! What's that noise outside?"

BOYS: "Now wonder who was beating on that pan."

GRANDPA: "Now's my time to teach the boys not to trifle with tacks."

GRANDPA: "Hello, boys! Now what is all this noise about?"

"Good Heavens! I've gone and hatched those China eggs."

ON THE DIAMOND

FLAMINGO BASEMAN—"These high ones are easy!"

Nervy Nat—"Now, isn't that disgraceful? If those married people would fight it out in their own flats—but to desecrate these sylvan shades and peaceful paths with their cheap infelicities—it's an outrage!"

Nervy Nat—"Stop! In the name of Dowie and Ella Wheeler Wilcox, stop! You madam, let go the proboscis; and you, you unregenerate, half-baked son of a polyp! raise not your shower-stick against your female helpscrap"—

Nervy Nat—"Well, if you persist. Now, madam, give him an uppercut and then run like— Oh, I've got him fast enough. He's as helpless as a Willie boy with three beers"—

Mrs. Scraper—"What have you got to do with it, anyhow, you impertinent wretch? I'll let you know I don't allow any one but myself to pull him around like that."

Nervy Nat—"Have done, you tabasco-tempered, peroxide shrew! Help!"

? ! ! ! ? ! ! ? ! ! ! ! ? ? ! ? ? ? ! !

The Cop—"Oi'll come back afther yez, me foine hobo, as soon as Oi hov these scrappy mugs in th' cooler."

Nervy Nat—"Suffering salamanders! that was a beautiful siesta. Catch me interfering between man and — beast again. It would be much simpler to lie right down in front of the 'Empire State express'."

A LOOK AHEAD
Coaching in the Horseless Age

"GOING DOWN?"

A FOURTH OF JULY SOLILOQUY
"Great fire crackers!—How I have grown since 1776!"

FOXY GRANDPA

HE HADN'T BEEN ON A BICYCLE FOR A LONG TIME, BUT NEVERTHELESS HE HAD NOT LOST HIS SKILL.

BOYS: "We will loosen the bolt on the front wheel. That will be a good joke on Gran'pa when he comes to ride."

GRANDPA: "Hello, boys. Here you are, just in time to help me on my wheel."

GRANDPA: "Now careful, boys. You know I haven't been on my wheel for a long time."

GRANDPA: "Goodness, boys, what is the matter? I must have forgotten how to ride."

GRANDPA: "Dear me, boys, I am losing my front wheel."

GRANDPA: "Ta, ta, boys, I won't bother with the other wheel. I see I have not quite forgotten how to ride."

INFLEXIBLE

"I'll never speak to them again!"

"Oh! You shouldn't get as cross as that, Flossie!"

"No. I won't speak to them again, and I'll tell them so every time I see them!"

STYLISH

"These doughnuts may not be fit to eat, but they certainly make a stylish collar."

LOCATING THE INJURY

THE CENTIPEDE—"I'm suffering from a broken leg, Doc."

HOUSE SURGEON—"Your suffering, sir, is likely to be prolonged if you don't be more specific! What number leg do you think it is?"

GOSSIP

"May has had no use for archery since she was married."

"No. She hit the mark!"

"Yes: an easy mark!"

" 'Cold feet are usually caused by indigestion brought on by over-eating.' There, Jimmy, now we know what's the matter of us!"

"TWO STRIKES AND THE BASES FULL"

"FANNED OUT"

THE CHAMPION

BARNYARD REASONING

"Bless me! if the old lady isn't eating tacks."
"Yes: I believe she's going to lay a carpet."

A BOY IN SPRINGTIME

"Dog gone it! I wish they hadn't found her till after the baseball season."

"Sunday Clothes"

A BOY IN SUMMERTIME

The Blowing-up of Penelope

NERVY NAT FLAGS A TRAIN

NERVY NAT—"It is nearly time for the three-thirty flyer. I will stop the train and have some fun with the engineer, who threw me off once."

NERVY NAT—"Stop! In the name of humanity, esoteric Buddhism, and the concert of the powers, stop! There's a wash-out on the line back here aways! Ah! they're putting on the brakes. She's slowing up. Gee! I hope I can keep a straight face."

ENGINEER—"My noble boy, shake! This proves there's many a hero's heart beating under a tramp's shirt."
NERVY NAT—"This is most embarrassing; but really, my dear chap, I hope you were not referring to me as a tramp. I may be a little rumpled, and I may need three or four shaves; but really, you know"—
ENGINEER—"There, there! Forget that I said it, my brave fellow! Now show us the wash-out."

ENGINEER—"I think the passengers would like to make up a handsome purse for you if they knew it was through your prompt and courageous act they are all alive this minute."
NERVY NAT—"I'm sure it is very kind of you to think of such a thing; but really, 'pon honor, I have very little use for money. I've sort of outgrown the habit of handling it, don't you know. We are nearly to the place."

NERVY NAT—"There is the wash-out on the line I was telling you about, gentlemen. I don't think you need to report it at headquarters, though. Awfully sorry, and all that sort of thing, if I've detained you."

NERVY NAT—"Such a rude set of men, those railroad employes. I am almost certain I've swallowed two of my twelve-year-old molars, three milk-teeth, eight gin and three seltzer teeth, and there are a couple of thank-ye-ma'ams on my skull that were level turf a while ago."

"WALL, HANK, I RECKON WE'RE GOIN' TO HAVE AN EARLY WINTER. THAT'S THE SECOND FLOCK OF RICH FOLKS I SEEN FLYING SOUTH."

"HONK!"

DEAD RECKONING

"Where are we cabby?"
"Nowhere. This is Brooklyn."

MR. JACK!

SH-H-H! I WANT TO SURPRISE MY HUSBAND MR JACK
MR JACK PRIVATE
1

GUESS WHO IT IS!
2

"AS IF I DIDN'T KNOW KITTY MY OWN LITTLE STENOGRAPHER NOBODY ELSE HAS SUCH A SWEET POPSY WOPSY CUNNING LITTLE HAND!"
3

"WHY JACK!"
4

"AH DIDN'T I PLAY A GOOD JOKE ON LITTLE WIFEY! AS IF I DIDNT KNOW YOU RIGHT AWAY!"
5

"OH JACK, I WAS AFRAID YOU THOUGHT IT WAS SOMEONE ELSE!"
SWINNERTON -03
6

THE FIRST AUTOMOBILE

A PICTORIAL SERMONETTE

On the Imaginative Man who works himself into a Passion because he thinks Some one may insult him.

"I wonder if he will remember me after all these years. Maybe his prosperity has changed him so that he will pretend to forget the old school-days."

"Well, if he tries the haughty act with me there'll be trouble. I won't allow any man to insult me. It would be an outrageous way to treat an old friend."

"And I'm too proud to stand for it a minute! I'll mop up the floor with him! I'll show him that I'm as good as he is, even if he is rich. Confound him, I'll leave this beastly hole rather than be humiliated that way!"

As a matter of fact Mr. Scadsworth was delighted to see his old friend.

WHAT IS THE MOST INTENSE HAPPINESS THAT A HUMAN CAN FEEL?

Is it This—*"Well, Bill, you won't have to hang tomorrow. The governor has signed your reprieve."*

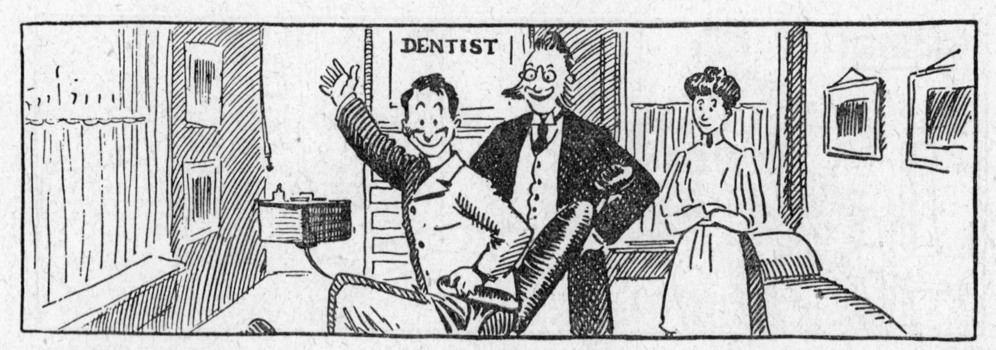

Or is it This—*"There! your last tooth is filled and you won't have to come again for years."*

Or is it This—*"Hooray, Charley! your ticket has won the capital prize in the lottery!"*

No, it is this.

MRS. SCADSWORTH GOES AWAY FOR HER HEALTH

THE DOCTOR—*"What you need, Mrs. Scadsworth, is lots of outdoor exercise—horseback riding, walking, mountain air."*

Mrs. Scadsworth arrives at the mountain resort and takes some exercise between the breakfast room and the card room.

Where she and her friends start a game of Bridge.

Which continues without interruption during her stay in the mountains.

MAUD! HOOLIGAN! ALPHONSE! GASTON! COUNT ALOYSIUS! GEE!

MR. HO. "I lost my balance as the street car started today and sat right into a monkey's lap."
MRS. HO. "Oh! I hope you apologized."
MR. HO. "No; it was too late, but I'm going to send a wreath."

The footall game was waxing hot, Thanksgiving Day was fair,
But Fluffy, seated near the lines, was verging on despair;
For one there was (just Brother Dick) whose violets she wore,
And, oh, the team that he was on seemed fated not to score!

Then, as the panting, swart faced crew pressed nearer, yard by yard,
The whistle blew and one big chap fell bleeding on the sward.
He bled not for the team she cheered, but pity was her guide,
And proffering her vinaigrette she called him to her side.

"He must not, must not, risk his life," she said with anxious frown—
And she hadn't worn his roses, for they didn't match her gown!
And so it went! How pale he was! That full back was to blame!
And soon she had that mangled warrior sitting out the game.

With envious brow a comrade gazed upon her gentle wiles;
Was he to bathe his face in mud, the other in her smiles?
He, too, had sent her roses, and he, too, would show his worth,
And soon his face had left its epidermis in the earth.

And there he sat with Fluffy, too! Then round that blessed spot
Grim heroes vied for welcome sprains' Did Fluffy know, or not?
I know she smiled, and this I know, that ere the half was o'er
The cripples that she gathered round her numbered more and more,

Until that recent all star team was mostly substitutes,
And fearful sisters whispered that the other side were brutes!
It matters not—the tide was turned, and, piling score on score,
The team won out whose quarter back had sent the flowers she wore.

And then—oh then! the joke began to filter through the crowd,
And both the teams sent up a cheer for Fluffy long and loud;
And round her coach they rolled each other's college yells on high—
But do you think that Fluffy ever, ever found out why?

AS HE LOOKED WHEN HE TRIED TO EXPLAIN IT TO THE BOYS AT HOME

TRYING TO SQUARE HIMSELF

"I CAN'T REACH IT, GRAN'PA." "TRY IT NOW, TOMMY."

THE GENTLE SEX

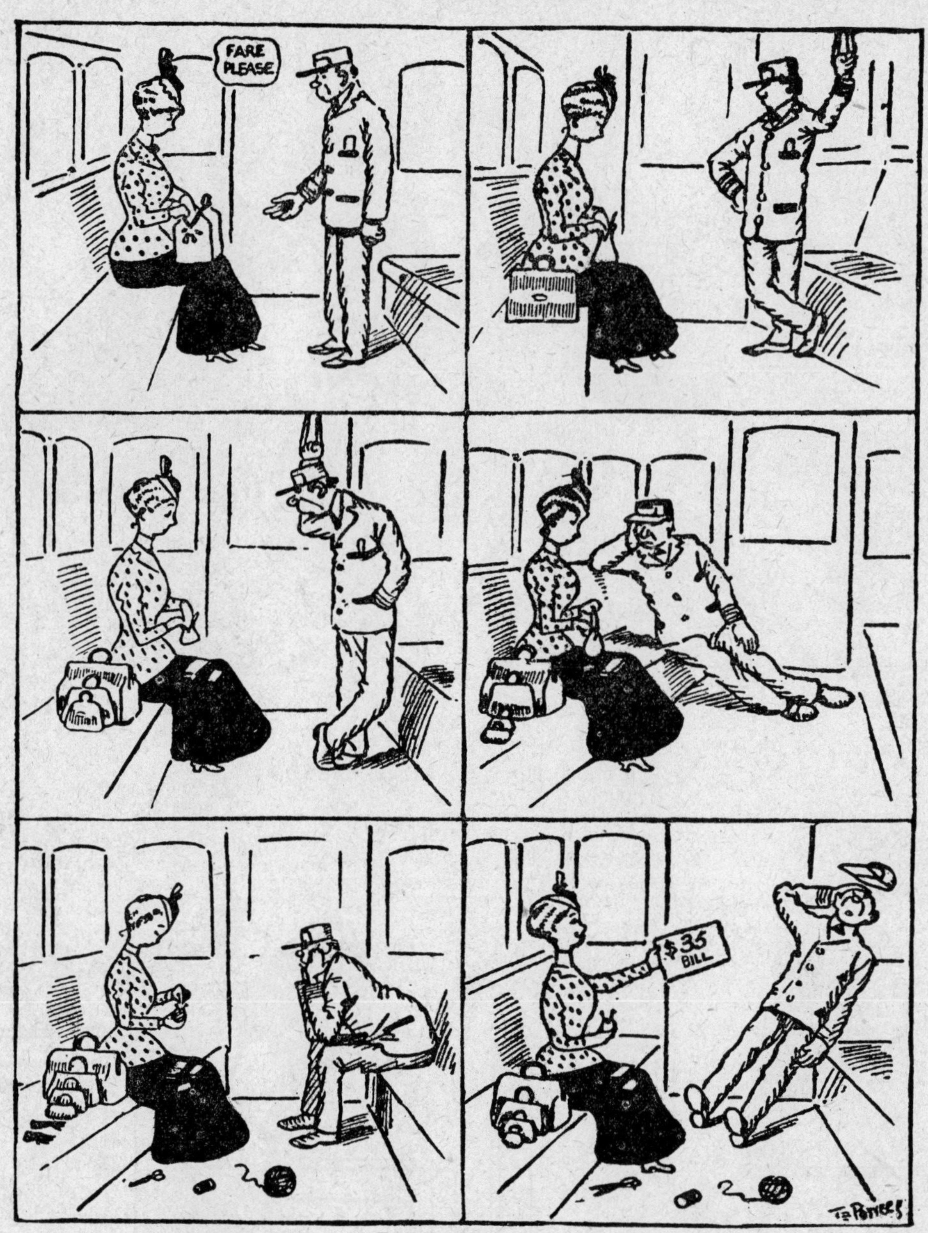

FARE, PLEASE

A LITTLE PROBLEM IN MILLINERY

"What do you think of his riding?"
"Bad form. Sits too far forward."

LO, THE POOR INDIAN

BOY—"What is the Indian looking for, Pop?"
HIS DAD (*with deep feeling*)—"For a decent cigar, in all likelihood, Willie."

"OH, IF YOU WERE ONLY A HORSE!"

LITTLE NEMO IN SLUMBERLAND
OH! YOU GOT IT BACK AGAIN. HOW DID YOU GET IT FLIP?
NEVER MIND ABOUT HOW I GOT IT! HOP IN AN' I'LL GIVE YOU A SPIN AROUN' THE BLOCK!
WATCH WHERE YOU ARE GOING! LOOK, YOU'VE KNOCKED OVER TWO ASH CANS!
THAT'S NOTHING! WHERE DO YOU WANT TO GO?
LETS GO UP IN THE PARK, BUT COME RIGHT BACK!
ALL RIGHT! I'LL SHOW YOU SOME TRICKS I CAN DO WITH THIS CAR OF MINE! SEE THOSE STAIRS?
IT GOES RIGHT UP AS EASY, DOESN'T IT? WITHOUT A BUMP!
RIDES LIKE A BOAT DOESN'T IT? TELL ME!
YES, BUT WATCH WHERE YOU ARE GOIN!
AW THAT'S ON-LY A WATER FOUNTAIN! UM DAT'S NUTHIN!
LOOK OUT! FLIP, YOU'LL RUN INTO THAT BUILDING!
WILL I? WELL YOU JUST WATCH ME! I KNOW THIS OLD MACHINE TOO WELL! WATCH!
SEE UP THERE! WATCH THIS BABY CLIMB UP THERE! WATCH!
OH! NAW! I'M AFRAID DON'T DO IT FLIP!
OH! I CAN GO ANY OLD PLACE WITH THIS! YOU NEEDN'T GET SCARED WITH ME!
I AM, FLIP, SCARED! GOOD AND SCARED! LETS NOT GO ANY FARTHER!
LETS GO BACK HOME FLIP COME! THIS IS TOO DANGEROUS FOR ME!
THERE IS NOTHING TO BE AFRAID OF! WE ARE ON TOP NOW!

HOW ARE WE GO-ING TO GET DOWN?
HA! HOW DID WE GET UP? DON'T WORRY! DON'T WORRY!
I BELIEVE I AM GOING TO CRY!
ONLY BABIES CRY YOU'RE NOT A BABY! BE GAME! DON'T BE A BABY!
I WILL IF YOU WILL PROMISE TO TAKE ME RIGHTHOME!
NIX ON ANY HOME. - RE-MEMBER, KID, YOU'RE WITH ME! TAKE IT EASY.
NOW ARE WE GOING HOME FLIP. EH? YES?
I JUST WANT TO SHOW YOU ONE MORE STUNT, THEN WE'LL GO HOME!
NO! NO. NO! FLIP! STOP! STOP! OH!
THERE YOU GO AGAIN! SIT DOWN! SIT DOWN!
I WANT TO GO HOME I WANT TO GO HOME!
STICK! STICK. MY BOY! RE-MEMBERYOU'RE WITH ME!
NO. YOU WONT. I'LL SQUARE IT WITH YOUR MOTHER! QUIT WORRYING
I'LL GET A LICKING FOR BEING SOAK-ED THIS WAY.
OH! I WAS DREAMING AGAIN! OH! WHEO!
WINSOR McCAY

"HURRAH! THE FIRST POTATO VINE IS UP"

HOME FROM HARVARD
The automobile is approved by the old man.

CHIPS FROM THE DIAMOND

THE REGATTA OF THE FUTURE

"GREAT SCOTT! I THOUGHT HE'D GONE TO AFRICA!"

GETTING EVEN

Burglar—"Not a thing in the place; but here's where I git even. I'll set his alarm fer t'ree o'clock."

GOOD ADVICE

Fond Mother—"Now, Willie, fly straight to school, and be careful that you are not run over by an aeroplane."

"ALL THE GNUS THAT'S FIT TO PRINT"

" 'Hould th' wire' says he, Begorry! next toime he can come here an' hould it himself."

WHEN THE NEWS OF PRESIDENT ROOSEVELT'S VISIT REACHED AFRICA

Officer: I KETCHED THIS HERE MUTT PINCHIN' BANANAS OFF A FRUIT STAND
Magistrate: AHA! 'PERSONATING AN OFFICER! TWO YEARS

AS GOOD AS THE BEST OF THEM

His Wife—"Do you know, John, this is the first time I've really enjoyed riding in this thing since you got it?"

"How can you sleep so late in the morning?"
"Just will power, Mother."

THE ADVANCEMENT OF WOMAN

THE HALL ROOM BOYS

They Are Simply Rolling in Wealth—in the Moving Pictures

GETTING SQUARE WITH MAUD!

(Continued on next page)

GETTING SQUARE WITH MAUD! (continued)

THAT'S WHAT THEY ALL SAY

IT MIGHT HAVE BEEN WORSE

If you should ask me, whether Dante
Drank Benedictine or Chianti,
I should reply, "I cannot say,
But I can draw him either way."

I'm told the Artist who aspires
To draw Forbes-Robertson requires
A Sargent's brush. Dear me! how sad!
I've lost the only one I had.

THE ONLY WAY

Speaker—"The only way we can gain woman's suffrage is by making an appeal through our charm, our grace, and our beauty."

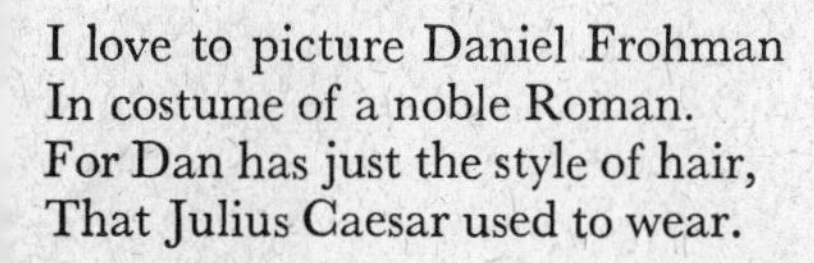

I love to picture Daniel Frohman
In costume of a noble Roman.
For Dan has just the style of hair,
That Julius Caesar used to wear.

I once called Bernard Shaw, in rhyme,
"The Greatest Playwright of his time."
Next day he cabled "Incorrect,
For 'his' read 'all,' " signed Shaw—Collect.

Mouse: LET'S GO IN AND BUST UP THE MEETING

"If man is the producer and woman the consumer, will Prof. Divine kindly name the sex of the fat party in the middle."

" 'I Gorry, I'm tired!"
"There you go! *You're* tired! Here I be a-standin' over a hot stove all day, an' you workin' in a nice cool sewer!"

NOTICEABLE

"You look stouter than you did at the last Convention."
"Do I? Must be the heavy underclothes I'm wearing."

"THERE, BUT BY THE GRACE OF GRAFT, SIT I."

PLAYING TO EMPTY SEATS

"DEY'S WOIMS IN IT!"

AT THE END OF THE WAR
St. Peter: "I've got a full house!"
The Devil: "You lose. I've got four kings!"

"What's the celebration about, M's Milligan?"

"Sure, me boy's comin' home today. He was sentenced to ten years in the penitentiary, but he got three years off for good conduct."

"Ah! I wish *I* had a son like that!"

THE LADY: "I THOUGHT THERE WAS TO BE A FUNERAL HERE."
THE CLERGYMAN: "THERE WAS A FUNERAL HERE, BUT IT WAS HELD EARLIER IN THE DAY."
THE LADY: "CAN YOU TELL ME IF THERE IS TO BE ANOTHER FUNERAL ANYWHERE THIS AFTERNOON?"

"Your Honor, this woman gave birth to a naked child!"

THE POET'S PLAINT

"I don't seem to be able to create anything! Nothing that will live, anyway."

STYLES FOR MEN, 1915

WHEN A FELLER NEEDS A FRIEND

Tad's Favorite Indoor Sports

Tad's Favorite Indoor Sports

PART TWO

World War I and the Impudent Decade

THE LIGHTER side of warfare is greatly exaggerated. To tell the truth, military humor is almost nonexistent, a fact borne upon me with particular force as I ransacked the graphic deposits of World War I. Aroused to further inquiry I pursued the subject historically, only to confirm a terrible commonplace known to every man on the firing line, on or under the sea, and in the air: war is not funny. My experience as Seaman Second Class in the First World War taught me that among sailors preparing for action, real humor is a very scarce article; and my brother—a colonel in the army—has assured me that a soldier's humor depends on the proximity of the battle line. At the training camp, there is always some smart undergraduate or stripling reporter who reflects the raw levity of the unadjusted recruit, but as the zero hour draws nigh, the forced levity dissolves into silence or, if not that, into grim, unprintable wit. Wars, I repeat, are not funny; not the present conflict, not the war that we won and lost, not any war that has ever been fought. The lighter side of warfare is largely wishful grinning on the part of 4-F editors.

At the outbreak of War I, popular excitement was inflamed with romantic passion, and the boys departed to the sound of trumpets and the sighs of pretty girls. But beneath the demonstrations ran a current of skepticism which nothing could hold in check, not the final victory, and, much less, the treaty of peace. To consolidate public opinion, and "to sell the war to America," powerful "drives" were organized in which every device known to existing propaganda was employed, from parades to posters. I have reason to remember those drives—I took part in them. Whenever we went ashore in the expectation of liberty and the pursuit of happiness, a war-bride ensign was sure to parade us up Fifth Avenue to lend a martial note to some high-pressure campaign on behalf of food conservation, recruiting, or the sale of Liberty Bonds. The mob on the side lines cheered itself hoarse and dropped lighthearted quips of praise. Not till then did I know how brave I was. But I give you my word that I never heard a humorous remark from those marching sailors—what they said would add warmth but not mirth to a book of humor.

For the paucity of military humor in this collection I make no apologies and no reproaches. Many a good man tried his hand at it, but the less said about his drawings the better. The artists of the comic strip soldiered in more ways than one; and Mutt and Jeff, after induction, were poor privates and worse comedians. A distant laugh echoes from LeRoy Baldridge's book of sketches, *I Was There;* the jokes in Captain Percy Crosby's illustrations of army life overseas do not misfire; and Wallace Morgan's vivid studies of the A.E.F., though intended purely as descriptive records, contain drawings which will pass the test of humor. The funniest artist produced by the war was Bruce Bairnsfather, the Scottish creator of Ole Bill, a character who, in retrospect, was almost as native to Americans as Denys Wortman's Mopey Dick. An English Tommy, in talking with me about Bairnsfather, avowed that Ole Bill was utterly impossible in the British army, and that he was popular in the States because Americans loved a streak of vulgarity in their humor. We shall have to consider the source of that remark and then skip it. All I know is that some years ago, Captain Bairnsfather, on an American tour, delivered two illustrated lectures per diem for 365¼ days—net results $50,000—before audiences composed of the women Helen Hokinson draws, and less vulgar women are not to be found anywhere, not even in England.

The great victory over the Germans and the valor of our troops abroad were wasted in the domestic battles following the armistice. The mistakes made after the cessation of hostilities need not be enumerated: today those mistakes are the concern of all thinking men and women. The severity of the terms of the peace treaty were denounced by professors and historians now busily eating their words, and the League of Nations was rejected by isolationist Senators. With single-minded fury the American people resolved to forget the war and go about their business: "to return to normalcy," as Harding voiced it.

Culturally and economically the turgid years of normalcy were characterized by a dissolution of human values the like of which had not been seen since the Babylonians went haywire. There were two tendencies of behavior, bilateral and continually at war with each other. The first was a pregnant materialism ending in Babbittry and ruin; the second, in the apt words of Frederick Lewis Allen, was "the revolt of the high-brows." Let us look at them in order.

The war was followed by the machine age which, in centralized wealth and social extravagance, made the prodigality of the gilded age of the nineties seem no more than the crude gestures of pioneers and amateurs. Millionaires abounded everywhere, cost-plus millionaires who had battened on the government, and other barons of wealth created by new industries such as the automobile, the manufacture of electrical machinery, and not least, the movie. With wealth came political power, antiliberalism, social arrogance, and moral indignation which served as the mask for insane physical indulgences.

The Prohibition amendment, the established law of the land, was circumvented with barbaric glee by all classes alike and drinking passed into the control of bootleggers and speakeasies. Prohibition was a national joke, the stock-in-trade of cartoonists, and stigmatized, once for all, in Rollin Kirby's drawing of the repugnant snooper. And the criminals preying upon liquor, the hijackers and large-scale beer barons like Al Capone, were also depicted by our artists with a jocularity that stunned European visitors, one of whom remarked to me, "I don't see anything funny in crime." The visitor may have been right, at that, but the fun engendered by normalcy was anything but normal. People drank who had never touched a drop, and temperate consumers now drank as if they should never drink again.

The fads, manias, and mechanized relaxations of the decade are hard to believe today in a nation sobered, or partly sobered, by an all-out war. The high cost of living was also a national joke. It was complained about and then facetiously dismissed as the H.C.L., for it made little difference to a country apparently rolling in money. The automobile was the great desideratum, and installment buying spread like a contagion. In every town a friendly loan association trafficked in cars, and the signs read, "Borrow and drive on." When Henry Ford exhibited his Model A, in 1927, millions of speed-crazy Americans turned out to see the wonders it performed. As the event of the year, it was second only to Lindbergh's flight to Paris.

The automobile carried speeding sinners to jazz dances and roadhouses fifty miles from home, and made practicable the garish country club where duffers in plus-fours swung their sticks under the tutelage of professionals. The craze for sports virtually eliminated the amateur, insured the solvency of colleges, and lifted boxing to its financial peak, the million-dollar gate. Athletes, not statesmen, were the popular heroes: Babe Ruth, Bobby Jones, Red Grange, Bill Tilden, Dempsey and Tunney, famous in song and story. Not less triumphant was the businessman, the apostle of Rotary and good-fellowship, the slave of deals and slogans, the man who had bartered his spiritual birthright for a piece of property—George F. Babbitt himself. Sinclair Lewis added his name to the language and the name is now a common noun. But this glorified money-grubbing, this hocus-pocus about advertising, this cult of materialism and creature comforts — all this, at bottom, was an affirmation of democracy rather than a denial. It was an outgrowth of the old equalitarian belief that everyone was entitled to his share of worldly goods, but transcending the bounds of common sense, it came to mean that every person should get more than his share of wealth, and that the getting should be an ideal, a career, not a means to a more estimable life.

The Babbitts ran the country. Possessing wealth and power, they controlled the votes and represented the majority—but their way of life was not unchallenged. Insidious forces were organizing, and when the revolt came, it was a pitched battle of prolonged fierceness and intensity, the most slaughterous campaign against materialistic culture ever waged in America. The leader of the revolt was H. L. Mencken, of Baltimore, newspaperman, editor, master of English prose, and the best polemical writer in forty-eight states. By right of intelligence and energy, Mencken was the acknowledged leader, and when, in 1924, he founded *The American Mercury,* the organ of "the civilized minority," with George Jean Nathan as coeditor, none dared lock horns with him. He kept his temper; his vocabulary of invectives was enormous and dreadful; and he owed no obligation to anything save his own conscience. *The American Mercury* was brilliantly edited, and in its palmy days was the most persuasive, and the most enjoyable, magazine in the country.

The American Mercury printed no illustrations. Mencken had a poor opinion of latter-day painters and, though receptive to cartooning, regarded it as less salutary than his verbal batteries. From this situation, you will see that the rising comic talent of the post-war decade—the bright young artists hovering between the Babbitts and the high-brows, coveting the lucre of the one and the superiority of the other—had no vehicle for their cleverness. Some worked for *Life,* but with caution, for *Life* was growing old gracefully, and in no mood to lift its skirts to shock the old lady from Dubuque.

The old-timers, McCutcheon, Ding, Tad, Fisher, Dirks, and Herriman, stuck to the newspapers, creating an art of and for the people; and whatever crimes they may have committed against good taste and good drawing, they were never guilty of snobbery. I may as well point out here and now that the old-timers and their successors in the comic strips were the men who kept alive the strains of native humor—the wandering, plotless fable, chock-full of absurdities and funny human quandaries. The humor of the strips is running thin and low at the moment, but one cannot hope for replenishment in times of war.

The new makers of the strips, heedless of the ruction between the Babbitts and the high-brows, went merrily on their way, but not exactly in the direction set by the founding fathers. Instead of fashioning preposterous creatures, they adhered more closely to actualities and kept their eyes on errant youth. Let us look at a couple of the most flourishing narratives. Frank King opened up *Gasoline Alley* in the summer of 1919, introduced the foundling Skeezix in 1921, and the strip is still going strong. Imagine allowing a thing with a name like that to live and grow up, to graduate from school and engage itself to a girl called Nina Clock, to work for a newspaper, to enlist in the army, and finally, to be sent overseas! Yet I report only the cold facts when I say that millions and millions of readers have followed this character from its infancy to its uniform, awaiting each episode with eagerness and suffering no disappointments. And why? Well, who knows? My opinion is that *Gasoline Alley* is soundly conceived—that the underlying idea is dear to the hearts of the young. It is a parable in pictures, telling the world that any boy can go places if he makes up his mind, and the parable is told with plenty of fun.

Shortly after War I, Carl Ed, a sports cartoonist, gave us *Harold Teen,* who, by the dispensation of art, remains a perpetual youth. Harold is the favorite of jerks and jitterbugs, of boys with changing voices and girls who stand before the mirror for hours scrutinizing the effectiveness of the sweater. Waving his streamlined fedora, he packs the jerks in his stripped-down, marked-up jalopy and they all go to town. The characters of this black-and-white joyride—Pa and Ma and Josie the kid sister, Lillums, Horace the egg-head, Pop Jenks, and Aunt Pruny—converse in authentic slang for the very good reason that Carl Ed, besides having a good ear, lives in a college town and collects the coinages fresh from the mint. But it is a fluid jargon, here today, gone tomorrow, and a little trying on the entrails, at least on mine. Right now the strips are starving for vertebrate slang, sharp masculine stuff like Tad's speech or, better still, the language of George Ade.

Ade was the Shakespeare of slang. That is not my metaphor, but one bestowed on him by the British when he was sojourning in London. He was not a boaster and the attention shown him by the cognoscenti embarrassed his modesty—but he was equal to the occasion. Andrew Lang gave him an at-home and among the guests were overeducated fellows and a number of tea-drunkards de luxe. The scholars prevailed on Ade to give them an exhibition of his literary skill, suggesting that he translate a piece of classic English into slang. Andrew Lang selected for the test the concluding words of Macaulay's essay on Warren Hastings. I am a trifle rusty in my Macaulay, but the classic bit reads substantially as follows: "For all his faults, and they were neither small nor few, there was only one cemetery that was considered worthy to hold his remains."

Pen in hand, Ade warmed up to the job, the guests noisily drinking tea and munching crumpets whilst awaiting the translation. They soon had it, and here it is, word for word—I am not rusty in George Ade: "For all his rough work, and believe me, he could pull off some fast ones, there was only one boneyard that was up to his class when it came to putting him away." Which is more expressive and more resonant English than Lord Macaulay ever wrote.

We know what Milt Gross would do to Macaulay, if he should return to the mad style of parody which he evolved in 1926, the year of *Nize Baby* and *Hiawatta.* He would break down the balanced sentences and convert them into the flabbergasting speech once so delightful to metropolitan audiences. The language is not slang but American-Yiddish dialect skillfully worked out and extremely funny to those who can read it without effort. To me it is hard going, and by the time I have deciphered it, the humor is dead. Milt Gross is a true comedian, and no mistake, but I prefer his drawings to his dialect.

Percy Crosby's *Skippy* has been around a long time, and has grown, I regret to say, a little the worse for wear. The boy first appeared in Gibson's *Life,* where his spontaneous mischief made him a pint-size hero despite the fact that he always came to grief because his desire to be tough exceeded his capacity. In the daily strip, Skippy is still a gallant little character, but his brooding recklessness seldom involves him in anything more exciting than routine misdemeanor.

In the conflicting forces of the impudent decade, Clare Briggs was content to cast his lot with the hale and hearty Americans who were neither Rotarian backslappers nor heathen intellectuals. He was influenced by McCutcheon, both in style and subject matter, but that is nothing against him: the borrowings were lawful and his best work was his own. Briggs delineated the humors of golfers and poker players, the irritations of domestic life, and the memories of boyhood, investing his drawings with the muscular enthusiasm and kindliness of his personality. So vast was his popularity that nobody, except the sour intellectual, would begin the day without looking at *Mr. and Mrs., Ain't It a Grand and Glorious Feeling?, When a Feller Needs a Friend,* and *The Days of Real Sport.* After his death, in 1930, the strip *Mr. and Mrs.* was continued, and I shall glance at it tomorrow morning. But the humor of the strip has dried up and it is only a cynical mess. They say that it is drawn by Briggs' ghost, but I have my doubts. I don't think that anyone draws *Mr. and Mrs.* now; it is self-spawning and it will go on and on until something kills it. Every day, at the crack of dawn, I look at it, always praying that the Greens will have taken their unending quarrels into the divorce court, and that I may never behold their snarling faces again.

Briggs' place in the cartoon cavalcade has been filled by H. T. Webster, author of *The Timid Soul, The Thrill That Comes Once in a Lifetime, Life's Darkest Moment, The Boy Who Made Good,* and *Bridge.* Webster deserves his public: he knows what people are up to; has ideas and does justice to them; and his drawings of a boy's adventures in the horse-and-buggy days are genuine Americana. I have never played a game of bridge nor have I seen one played, but from Webster's cartoons I know what bridge players are like and what the game has done to the Occidental branches of the human race. As concerns *The Timid*

Soul, I might say that something of Caspar Milquetoast dwells in all of us—that is why we respond to the pictures of him—but I have grown weary of that staggering, spineless biped, and I wish that he would do something manly for once in his life, and then die of fright.

The postwar decade, with its flowing wealth and cultural animosities, produced a class of Americans whose humorous behavior we are now prepared to examine. Those Americans were neither Babbitts nor high-brows; they were a set of metropolitans, New Yorkers to be specific, the bright boys and girls about town—and they were anything but lost. They knew all the answers and loved nothing so much as a well-turned crack against the yokels; they were the "sophisticates" of society, to use a noun which must have been coined by Warren G. Harding.

The boys and girls about New York had wit, enthusiasm, and a playful attitude toward all the serious enterprises of life, but no organ in which to display their talents comfortably. When *The New Yorker* was founded in 1925, they rejoiced in their good fortune, and sold themselves into the business of urbanity. *The New Yorker* was off to a discouraging start, owing in part to the gag line on the cover: "Not for the Old Lady from Dubuque," a negative appeal to the sophisticates in the provinces.

But the editor, Harold Ross, knew what he was driving at and nothing could dissuade him from his purpose. He concentrated on sophistication and made it pay, and through the years *The New Yorker* has been the vehicle for scribes and artists trained in what is now a tradition of self-conscious urbanity.

The irreverence of *The New Yorker* was not aimed at shams, social villainies, or the obnoxious strutting of big-town swells; it was, by fixed and supervised cunning, a system of brilliant raillery—the kidding of social errors, the harmless mockery of big business, the ridiculing of fictitious alcoholics, Boy Scouts, petting parties, night clubs, and the manners and diversions of middle-class provincials. This system has been closely guarded for twenty years, but of late, there are signs of change. *The New Yorker* is now giving serious thought to political matters and the shape of the world to come.

From the year of its inception, *The New Yorker* has been distinguished for the quality of its illustrations. It began with a nucleus of young artists of proved ability who were working gingerly for less venturesome journals: Rea Irvin, Peter Arno, Gluyas Williams, John Held, Jr., Barbara Shermund, and Helen Hokinson, and to this group others were added from time to time, Alfred Frueh, Ralph Barton, Otto Soglow, Alan Dunn, George Price, R. Taylor, William Steig, and Charles Addams. The artists were allowed to kick up their heels joyfully, each in his own style, there being but one reservation, the editor called the tune. Individuality was exploited for all it was worth, but no artist, however gifted, could belong to the coterie unless his work conformed to the editorial pattern. The ideas and subjects were submitted or prescribed, and when the drawing was finished, it was instantly recognizable as something only *The New Yorker* could conceive and produce. It is not exaggerating the case to say that *The New Yorker*, year in and year out, has printed more high-grade graphic humor than any other magazine in America.

Conceived in the spirit of the boulevards, *The New Yorker* departed from the old tradition of American humor, the tall tales and outlandish fables, which survive in the comic strips, and developed the funny idea with a witty, one-line caption to clinch the joke. The one-line caption had been used before, but sparingly and never with such originality and intelligence. The most pointed drawings of *The New Yorker* present an idea or predicament that screams for clarification. The drawing alone, more often than not, is enigmatical, but in conjunction with the surprising title beneath it becomes explosively funny. And the fun is clean. Though far from squeamish, this clever magazine has never played upon seductiveness or trafficked in nudity. That again is smart editing. In these days almost anything is printable, and bawdiness, for a time, may tempt the crowd, but as a staple it is boring stuff. Some of Peter Arno's drawings are intimate enough, but if anything, they are attacks on sex, violently funny but not provocative.

I may say, in this connection, that the charms of sex have never found their way into American cartooning. There has been a plethora of nudity on sale, some of which has been suppressed, but nothing to match the spontaneous gaiety of the prewar French magazines, *La Vie parisienne* and *Sourire*. The closest approach to the French acceptance of sex appeal appeared in the drawings which Nell Brinkley used to make for the *New York Evening Journal*.

As an example of the importance of the gag line to the humor of *The New Yorker*, I refer you to Carl Rose's drawing of the obdurate little girl and her mother at the dinner table. "It's broccoli, dear," the cajoling mother insists, and you know the answer: "I say it's spinach, and I say the hell with it!" That gag has gone round the world, and only a few weeks ago it cropped out in the *New York Herald Tribune*, where an editorial sage confirmed the forcibly fed brat's denunciation. It would seem that the promoters of greenery and essential still life fastened on the wrong weed, scientists having proved that spinach is a fraud and less rich in iron, mineral salts, and whatever it takes to make bad temper than a parcel of fresh timothy.

Gluyas Williams, a veteran of *The New Yorker*, was influenced in technique and in the wordless continuity by Bateman, of London. Williams is a droll fellow with a sturdy command of line, but I find his silent strips of a child getting ready for bed, or an old codger's pompous excursion to the vaults of a bank only to find the safe-deposit box empty, long drawn out and monotonous. He is most amusing in the static humor of his *Industrial Crises—The Day a Cake of Soap Sank at Procter & Gamble's,* let us say—and in his pictures of Coolidge at the White House. With his dry, pawky style, Williams was perfectly equipped to work on Coolidge, and his drawing of the President's refusal to leave the Executive Mansion until his galoshes were mated will keep green the memory of a man who, otherwise, should be forgotten. I have only one serious grievance against Williams: the faces of his men tend to fall into one cast, and that cast reminds me of Calvin Coolidge—which is enough to take the joy out of life.

Alfred Frueh, a funny man any way you take him, was known to observant New Yorkers ten years before the magazine of that name was born. In 1915, he held an exhibition of caricatures which were the finest things of their kind America had produced—straight caricatures, without literary embellishments, gag lines, or decorative accessories. Most of them were not made to order but to please Frueh's creative faculty, which was sometimes relieved by wood carving. I remember the one of George M. Cohan, a swaggering silhouette with straw hat and stick, the face a single curve without features, but Cohan to the life and all that he represented.

Ralph Barton, who died in 1931 at the age of forty, was a distinguished provincial from Kansas City, and the most gifted fop I have ever known. He came to New York in his nineteenth year and was never without commissions, admirers, and money. Born mature, he consented to no development; amazingly facile, he worked at night with intoxicating rapidity; at home in Paris, he outfopped the French at their own game, dressed like something midway between a toreador and an aesthete, and had many imitators among the young caricaturists. He illustrated Anita Loos' *Gentlemen Prefer Blondes*, Balzac's *Droll Stories*, and two affected books of his own composition; parodied the news in pictures and text for *Liberty*; designed advertising brochures between daybreak and breakfast; painted first-nighters on drop curtains; and made caricatures for *Vanity Fair* and *The New Yorker*—a full career, but not a happy one. All his work was caricature, overrefined, scintillating, and unlabored, with humorous appurtenances and faces remarkable for exaggerated characterization.

The gin-drinking levity of the jazz decade, with its headlong plunge into the lees of wantonness, is admirably summarized in the work of John Held, Jr. The cuties in bobbed skirts, the insatiable neckers and social bootleggers, the knock-down-and-drag-out parties in the penthouse, the fads and style—these were Held's themes, and he rendered them in deft, fragile drawings for *Liberty* and *The New Yorker*. He was a very popular artist while the fun lasted, but when the depression closed the doors on frivolity, he made no effort to live on his reputation. Instead, he called it a career, took seriously to painting, became an excellent water-colorist, and, by latest reports, was teaching art in a university.

Rea Irvin, a prolific contributor to the old

Life, was one of the founders of *The New Yorker*, and has remained one of its most exemplary humorists. There is an element of composure in his fun—it will not send you into stitches of laughter, nor will it let you down—and his drawings of *Social Menaces*, though aimed satirically at fashionable busybodies, contain no malice. Irvin works with equal sureness in cover designing, single cartoons, and the strip, and is likely to drag into each of them his most laughable subject, the blustering dowager who makes a public nuisance of herself.

Some years ago, when the depression was in full blast and humor at a premium, I served on a jury impaneled to select the half-dozen outstanding illustrated books of the year. It was a dull assignment. All the books were illustrated by the wrong people, and the good artists, worn down to drudges, were trying to get their second wind. And then, like a sea breeze in a soap factory, a book blew in, *The Little King*, by a little man named Otto Soglow. What a pleasure it was to give that sly, pocket-size masterpiece the badge of honor, to set it above and apart from the dismal tomes offered in the name of High Art!

The Little King, of course, was not a stranger. He had reigned in the pages of *The New Yorker* and had played at pantomime in musical comedies, but it was good to see him in a book. Soglow has created other characters, and his imagination is seldom idle, but the speechless little monarch will probably not be displaced in popularity. To dissect the King's appeal would be an impertinence, but it is worth while to look into the nature of Soglow's humor, for it is a very rare brand indeed. His Little King is a purely imaginary being and, as such, might have taken his place in the early comic strips had he been merely an innocent adventurer. But he is not innocent; he is a sophisticated character and his sleights, schemes, and attitude are not only modern but urban. Thus he carries the old type of comedy into the new. As a craftsman, Soglow knows the value of suspense in planning his sequences, draws with a concise rhythmical flourish, and never wastes a drop of ink. The Little King was born for the comic strip, and he is there today, as everybody knows.

As the postwar era ran dizzily onward, the country had never been more prosperous or the economy more stable. The trading in stocks was unprecedented, and young brokers with college degrees, bond salesmen, and lay gamblers made money hand over fist. Factories boomed, turning out the marvelous toys and material conveniences invented by technological genius: radios, vacuum cleaners, oil burners, a frigidaire for every icebox, and two cars for every garage.

The dark side of the picture was lost in the effulgent orgy of riches and brainless living. It was not known then but it is known today that the average income was pitifully low and unskilled labor underpaid; that bankers were gobbling up the farms, and share-croppers were living on sow bosom and corn bread, as they had always done. Not one of those evils disturbed the general feeling of security. On the cultural side, as the decade closed, changes were occurring, some of which indicated the return to a more sensible code of living, others merely the exhaustion of overstimulated desires. Freakish styles slowly disappeared; girls let their hair grow and abandoned the boyish figure; and the reaction against promiscuity augured a more seemly relationship between the sexes. The crusade against Babbittry tapered off when Mencken turned his thunder on the politicians, and when the stock market, soaring to unbelievable heights, excited the speculative instincts of everybody from elevator boys to the Chief Executive who had installed a private wire in the White House.

The country was heading for a fall, and you know what happened in October, 1929. The boys in our armed forces were impressionable children then, and need not be told of the millions of unemployed who walked the streets, the evicted families, closed factories, broken banks, unpaid teachers, lost savings, and all the rest. The Great Depression left its mark on them and when the war is over, we should do well to keep that in mind.

The last people to recognize the depression were the sophisticates, and the drift of humor in those dark days was still in the channels of urbanity. They tried to overlook the depression, then to forget it, then to divert attention from it. You cannot kid suffering, unemployment is nothing to laugh off, and poverty, like war, is not funny; but there was room, you would have thought, for a humorous side-swipe or two at some of the causes of suffering and at some of the voluptuaries and stinkers who sat tight and got tight and carried on unfeelingly until the arrival of better days. In short, it was the time for recrudescence of the comic morality which, as used by Opper and Davenport, was an instrument to lacerate social tumors. But Opper and Davenport and the people who loved their comedy were not sophisticates. When it came to humor, they were as vulgar as old Justice Holmes at the burlesque show. The Justice was eighty-five and the jokes were mellow; he clapped his hands and nudged the blonde at his side and exclaimed, "Thank God, I am a man of low tastes!"

"Well, if you knows a better 'ole, go to it."

A MOVING PITCHER

MOVIE OF A MAN AND A NIGHT THUNDERSTORM

SATURDAY, WHEN SUCKERS IS A BITING.

"DON'T FALL, HENRY, OR YOU'LL BREAK THE PICTURE"

GIRTH CONTROL

IRATE CAPTAIN—I say, Corporal Jenkins, have you seen my baggage about anywhere?
JENKINS—Yes, sir. She's talking with the Colonel over there!

ONE IN A THOUSAND

"—Oh! Look, lady, that's my boy, Jimmie!"

The Camouflaged Steed: I'VE OFTEN HEARD OF THE HORRORS OF WAR, BUT I NEVER EXPECTED TO BE ONE

COMBINING BEAUTY AND UTILITY; OR, SOME 1917 MODEL HATS

SECOND-LIEUTENANT AND PRIVATE TOMLINSON (OWN BROTHERS IN PRIVATE LIFE) MEET IN A SECLUDED SPOT

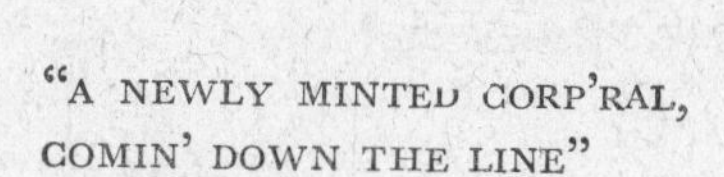

"A NEWLY MINTED CORP'RAL, COMIN' DOWN THE LINE"

HOW WE FORCED GERMANY INTO THE WAR

At least that is what he told his mother.

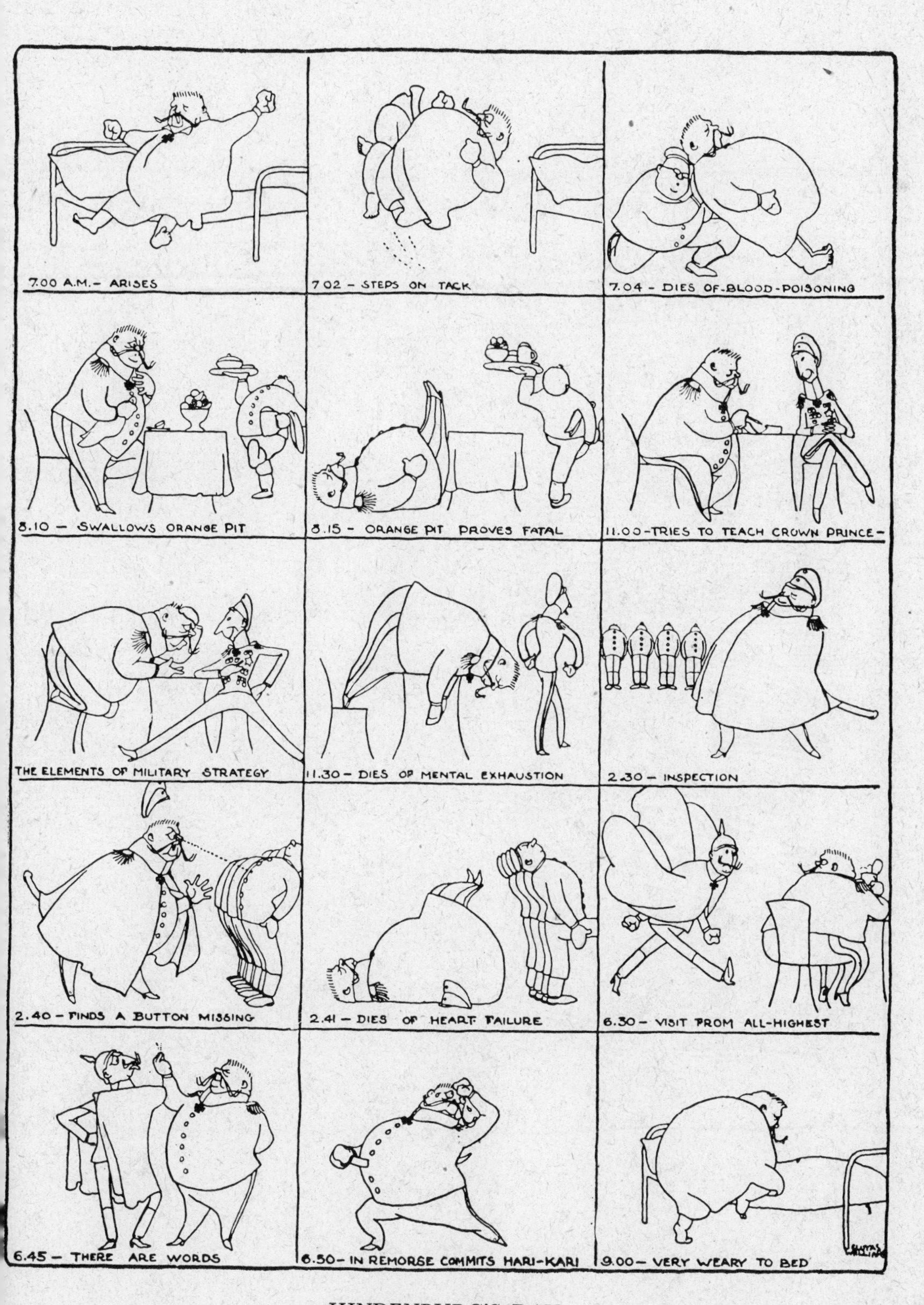

HINDENBURG'S DAY
According to the Press Reports

GOOD HEAVENS!!!
IMUST HAVE BEEN
AN AWFULLY SICK MAN
PICKLES
CRACKERS
P.L.° Crosby

"MY, HOW SHE HAS CHANGED!"

DOG-GONE IT

Monday Morning; Trotzky Executed by Lenine

Monday Afternoon; Lenine Beheaded by Trotzky

Tuesday Evening; Trotzky Addresses the Soviet

Wednesday Morning, Lenine Addresses the Proletariat

Thursday Morning; Trotzky Imprisoned in the Citadel

Thursday Night; Lenine Incarcerated in the Fortress of Peter and Paul

Friday Morning; Lenine Stebs Trotzky between the Volga and the Nevsky

Friday Afternoon; Trotzky Shoots Lenine in the Smolny Institute

Friday Evening; Comrades Lenine and Trotzky Discuss the Bourgoisie

A FEW DAYS WITH LENINE AND TROTZKY, ACCORDING TO THE NEWSPAPERS

"Say, Bill, do you know what we made out of the World War—we made 185 million dollars."

"I can't make up my mind whether to buy my wife a milkin' stool or a fryin' pan for Chris'mus."
"Why don't ye git her a nice new washtub, Hen?"

"NOW THEN, ALL TOGETHER, 'MY COUNTRY 'TIS OF THEE'"

If Senators Talked at Home as They Do in Congress

"My dear, will you have another cup of coffee?"

"The question at issue is one of Americanism as against un-Americanism, and I, thank God, am one hundred per cent American!" etc.

"The matter may seem small to some, but to me it threatens the very foundations of this great and glorious nation," and so forth.

"I shall now take time to read a short article of fifty thousand words on the culture of the coffee bean, which may or may not have some bearing on the case." He reads.

"After that, who can deny that those who oppose me in this matter are selfish, corrupt, partisan, unpatriotic and pro-German?" etc.

"And so on the question of whether or not I shall have another cup of coffee, I must, in justice to myself, my country and my constituents, vote Aye!"

SOMEBODY IS ALWAYS TAKING THE JOY OUT OF LIFE

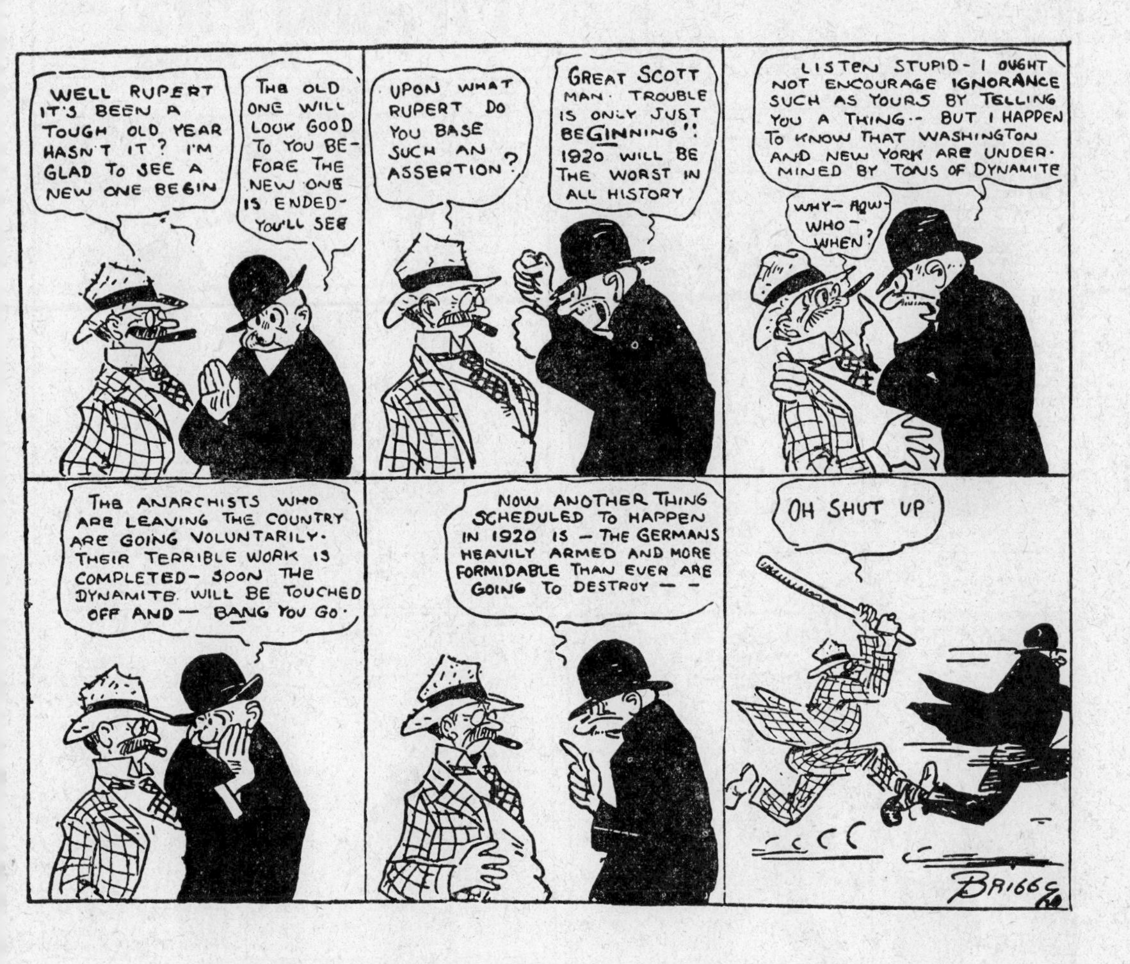

INVENTIONS OF PROFESSOR LUCIFER BUTTS

WE'RE RUINING THE CHILD BUT I CAN'T HELP IT
STOP LAUGHING! I'M TRYING TO DISCIPLINE HIM.
WON'T DO IT WON'T DO IT
Mr. and Mrs. —
By Briggs

OH - I'M SO GLAD YOU CAME HOME - I'VE SOMETHING TO TELL YOU
NOW WHAT!?

BERTRAM HAS BEEN AS NAUGHTY AS HE COULD BE AND I TOLD HIM WHEN YOU GOT HOME YOU'D PUNISH HIM
NOW LOOK HERE VI' I CAN'T DO IT -- I'M NOT IN THE MOOD

WELL YOU'VE GOT TO DO IT - - - YOU SHOULD TAKE SOME INT'REST IN HIM - - - HE NEEDS A FATHER'S DISCIPLINE
ALL RIGHT - ALL RIGHT!! WHERE IS HE?

BERTRAM - YOUR MOTHER SAYS YOU'VE BEEN NAUGHTY TODAY - COME HERE TO ME
I' CAN SPELL DOG POP

BERTRAM - I SHALL HAVE TO PUNISH YOU FOR BEING DISOBEDIENT
I WON'T DO IT AGAIN POP

GOSH - I'D RATHER GET A KICK MYSELF THAN DO THIS
ARE YOU GOING TO WHIP ME?

(CONTINUED)

YES- I SHALL HAVE TO PUNISH YOU BERTRAM — THERE! LET THIS BE A LESSON TO YOU

YOW-OO-OO! MA-MAMA
WHAT TH'-!!?

MY POOR BABY WHAT IS THE MATTER? ?.?? WHAT DID HE DO TO YOU?? COME TO YOUR MOTHER - DARLING
YOW-WOW WOW-OO-OO MAMA-MAMA

SHAME ON YOU - HOW COULD YOU HAVE THE HEART
YOU TOLD ME TO PUNISH 'IM DIDN'T YOU?- WHY I JUST TAPPED HIM EASY LIKE THIS- I DON'T THINK HE FELT IT
SLAP-

I DIDN'T TELL YOU TO MURDER HIM- POOR LITTLE HELPLESS CHILD
OH- DIDN'T YOU? WHY I THOUGHT YOU DID - YOU NEEDN'T EVER ASK ME AGAIN.

PAPA LOVE MAMA?
BRIGGS 3-14/20

A Day in the Life of the One-Note Man

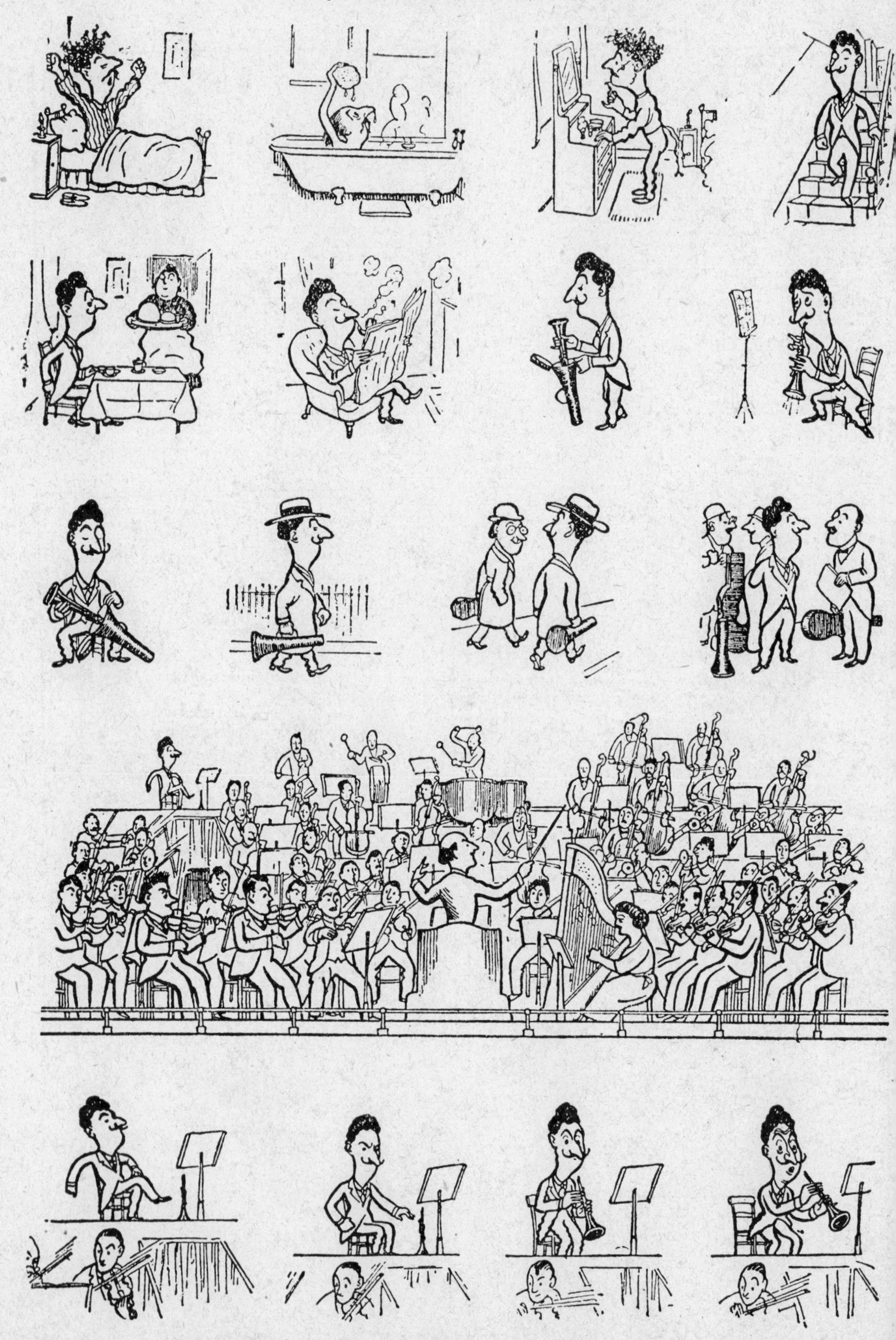

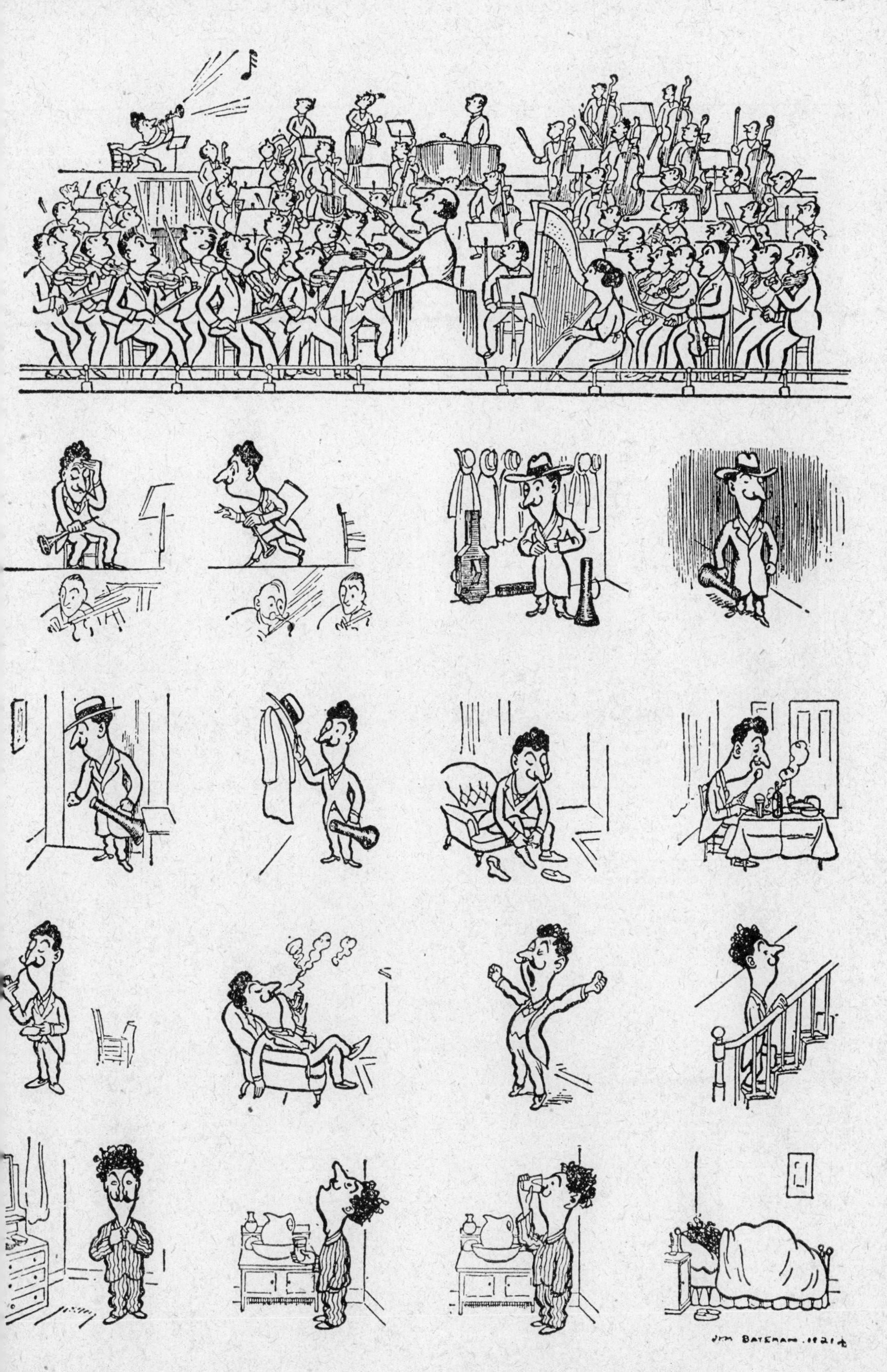
H M BATEMAN 1921

MUTT AND JEFF—Outspeeding Father Time

(CONTINUED)

WHAT D'YE MEAN, GIVE THANKS?
AIN'T THANKSGIVING COMING? YOU OUGHT TO GIVE THANKS THAT I LET YOU OFF SO EASY!

MERRY CHRISTMAS!! DON'T FORGET THAT WE'RE LIVING IN A FAST AGE!
?!

WHAT TH'-? PHOO!
HAPPY NEW YEAR! MY WORD, HOW TIME FLIES THESE DAYS!!
TAR

NIX, MUTT NIX! FOR THE LOVE OF MIKE, DON'T THROW THAT TAR ON ME!
APRIL FOOL!! I WASN'T GONNA THROW IT ON YOU.
TAR

DECORATION DAY IS COMING SO OF COURSE I HAVE TO DECORATE SOMETHING! TEE HEE!
TAR
6-26-

HOW STUPID OF ME TO FORGET WASHINGTON'S BIRTHDAY!
Fisher

GASOLINE ALLEY

AIN'T IT A GRAND AND GLORIOUS FEELIN'?

A VALENTINE

THE DAYS OF REAL SPORT

IT HAPPENS IN THE BEST REGULATED FAMILIES

BARNEY GOOGLE

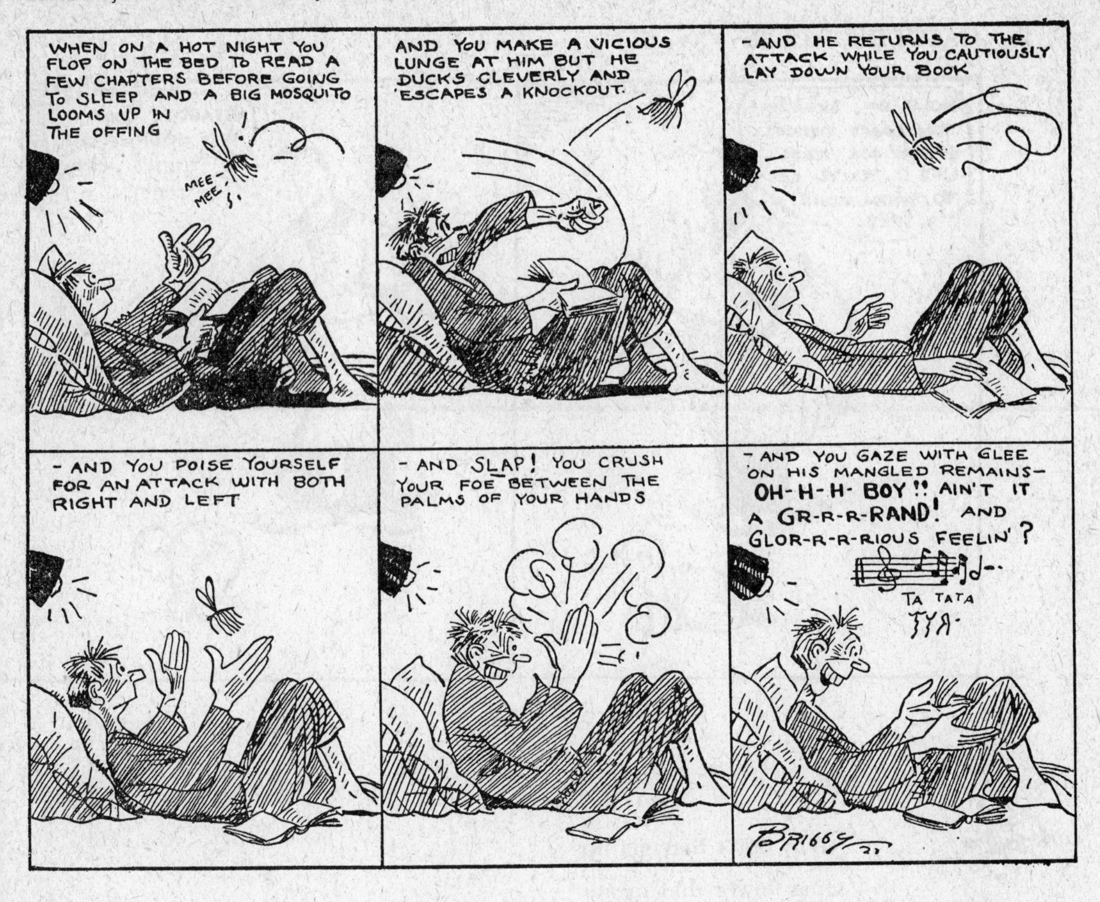

Sparky Is a Loving Old Soul

GASOLINE ALLEY

"Why don't they get up some flower that means a bust in the nose?"

"C'mon, Mary Pickford, an' git busy with them supper dishes!"

LEARNING TO SHIFT GEARS

Miss Gnu: "There goes Willie Kangaroo. He's broken off his engagement to Isobel Wallaby."
Miss Gazelle: "The little bounder!"

Tad's Favorite Outdoor Sports

BARNEY GOOGLE

Tad's Favorite Indoor Sports

Sparky Is a Loving Old Soul

Outdoor Sports
By Tad
I AINT FELT A BASEBALL FOR THREE WEEKS - ALL I DO IS SKIP THE ROPE, RUN ROUND THE PARK, GET A RUB DOWN AN' GO TO BED EARLY
SAME HERE - I QUIT A GOOD JOB IN A LUMBER CAMP TO BE A PITCHER - I SWAN THE WORK WAS EASIER THERE AND I'M DOIN' NO PITCHIN' HERE
PEPPER. SALT. MUSTARD. VINEGAR!!
38 39 THE HEAD MAN SAYS YOU GOTTA SKIP 200
COME ON JUMBO STEP!!
SHE WAS ONLY A PIANIST'S DAUGHTER BUT GEE!! SHE WAS HIGH TONED
OUTDOOR SPORTS
LAMPING TWO ROOKIES AS THEY COMPARE NOTES IN THE BIG LEAGUE CAMP DOWN SOUTH
TAD 3-18
© 1929, Int'l Feature Service, Inc., Great Britain rights reserved.

Tad's Favorite Indoor Sports

WHAT!!!! YOU SAY YOU'LL ALLOW ME $76 FOR MY OLD CAR - DIDN'T YOU TELL ME YOUR CARS HAD SUCH GREAT RE SALE VALUE? MY OLD CAR. LAST YEARS
YES I DID - BUT YOU MUST REMEMBER THAT WAS BEFORE THE FLORIDA BOOM AND THE DRY LAW WENT BLOOEY.
AND YOU MUST TAKE INTO CONSIDERATION THE FACT THAT PHILADELPHIA WAS LOOKED UPON AS A CINCH IN THE AMERICAN LEAGUE
ITS THE OLD ARMY GAME PHIL - YOU CANT BEAT IT. 3 TO WIN AND 3 TO LOSE BUT YOU NEVER CASH IN
A GUY WITH AN OLD CAR IS JUST A DEAD DUCK
APPLE SAUCE
INDOOR SPORTS
TRYING TO TURN IN YOUR OLD RATTLER FOR A NEW MODEL TO THE SAME MAN YOU BOUGHT FROM.
TAD 10-4
© Int'l Feature Service, Inc., Great Britain rights reserved.

"Chee, Annie, look at
de stars—thick as
bed-bugs!"

Indoor Sports -:- -:- By Tad

BREAST OF WEAL AN' FRIED ERSTERS!!! TAKE EM AWOI

CALF'S LIVER AND BACON

BUSTON PEARLS 15¢

LAMB STEW

Y'KNOW I WAS DOG-TIRED WHEN I GOT THIS FAR AND DECIDED TO DROP IN HERE FOR A CUP OF TEA - ISN'T IT AN ODD PLACE?

YES - YES - I DON'T LIKE THE NOISE OR THE SMELLS HERE THOUGH - I CAME INTO PHONE - I USUALLY LUNCH AT THE MAYBELLE

I'VE SEEN HER IN THIS JOINT BEFORE AN' THE BLOKE USUALLY PLAYS THE LUNCH WAGON - HE'S CHUCKIN' THE SWELL COMIN' HERE

YEAH - I KNOW 'EM THEY'RE NEIGHBORS OF MINE ONE'S TRYIN' TO OUTSWELL THE OTHER

INDOOR SPORTS — LISTENING TO A PAIR OF FOUR FLUSHERS AS THEY ACCIDENTALLY MEET IN A QUICK LUNCH DUMP.

MY GAL WAS AS PURE AS THE DRIVEN SNOW BUT SHE DRIFTED

TAD 12-19

Tad's Favorite Indoor Sports

"THE FIVE SENSES" -:- By Nell Brinkley

Then There's That "Sixth Sense" That Helps Us to Know When "the Enemy" Is Approaching . . . to Know When the Girl Who Says "No" Means "Yes" . . . and This!!!

AN EDUCATIONAL-TRAVEL REEL—By Kayo Tortoni

LITTLE JIMMY

Would you believe
that among the un-
tutored folk of
far off Tallo-Tallo,
soap is esteemed
as the finest of
appetizers?
You'll be interested
to learn that in Samayo
it is considered unfortunate to
be hit on the head by a cocoanut
G U R K

"HERE YARE
CATCH -"
"I GUESS I DON'T
LIKE LIT'L BOYS
ANYWAY."
SWINNERTON

WHEN A FELLER NEEDS A FRIEND

JERRY ON THE JOB

AIN'T IT A GRAND AND GLORIOUS FEELIN'?

Further Instructions Needed

"DO YOU LIKE KIPLING?"
"WHY—I DON'T KNOW. HOW DO YOU KIPPLE?"

BRIDGE

GEORGE, DEAR, YOU PLAYED PERFECT BRIDGE ALL EVENING! YOU'VE ALWAYS PLAYED A BRILLIANT GAME BUT THIS EVENING YOU OUTDID YOURSELF. THE FEW TIMES YOU WERE SET MY STUPID BIDDING WAS ENTIRELY TO BLAME. YOU'RE A MARVEL AND I'M PROUD OF YOU!
WHY, HELEN, I PLAYED LIKE A DUB! IT WAS YOUR PLAYING THAT PULLED US THROUGH. YOU REALLY PLAYED A FLAWLESS GAME FROM START TO FINISH. WORK, FOSTER, FERGUSON OR ANY OF THE EXPERTS COULDN'T HAVE PLAYED BETTER
DO YOU HEAR WHAT I HEAR?
HUSBAND AND WIFE
A PICTURE DRAWN ENTIRELY FROM IMAGINATION

WELL, OLLIE, I TOOK THE BOYS OVER FOR EIGHT BUCKS THIS EVENING! NOT BAD, EH?
LOVELY! AND YOU ARE GOING TO GIVE ME HALF AREN'T YOU?
THE AMATEUR
WELL, HOW MUCH DID YOU WIN OR LOSE TO-NIGHT?
CAME OUT EXACTLY EVEN TO A PENNY! PRETTY LUCKY AT THAT. BEFORE TH' LAST RUBBER I WAS 45 BUCKS OUT
$150 TO THE GOOD
THE VETERAN
WEBSTER

BRIDGE

I'M TRYING TO GET UP A COUPLE OF TABLES OF BRIDGE, DO YOU PLAY?
I PLAY AT IT! HAW! HAW!
PARDON ME, BUT DO YOU PLAY BRIDGE? I'M TRYING TO –
YES, IF YOU CAN CALL IT THAT. HA-HA-HA!
YOU PLAY BRIDGE OF COURSE, MISS KWEEL?
I ADORE IT BUT I PLAY A PERFECTLY WRETCHED GAME
DO YOU PLAY BRIDGE, MRS. AMPLE?
OH, DEAH NO! I MERELY PLAY AT IT!
DO YOU PLAY BRIDGE?
YES!
I NOT ONLY PLAY BRIDGE BUT I PLAY THE BEST —!!—☆—— GAME IN THIS CITY!
WEBSTER

BRIDGE

"What's he been doin'?"
"Overthrowin' the guvment."

ABIE THE AGENT

"Joe Goof! Take Off My Best Sheet This Instant!"

He Wants What's Coming to Him

WHAT WE'RE COMING TO

MOTHER: "Reginald! How Often Have I Told You Not to Play in the Mud?"

THE SKEPTIC ROOSTER—"That's right! Stand there like a fool! I suppose you think I don't know a hawk when I see one."

IPPY: Do ya know what ya nta do if a cop chases ya? Run e sixty 'n' when he gets right top of ya, drop down on ya nds 'n' knees 'n' he'll go head over teakettle.

FRIEND: Oh! I know somethin' better 'n' that! You get down on yer hands 'n' knees right in back of a cop 'n' I'll come up 'n' give him a shove. It always gets a laugh outa me.

FRIEND: Let's dig up a cop now 'n' I'll knock him for a row of rollin' butter tubs. Just get behind him 'n' I'll do all the rest.

SKIPPY: Ask yer mother if ya can come out by me a little while. I wanta show ya some fireworks.

"After all, maybe I am a little too quick with me tongue."

GASOLINE ALLEY

"AND NOW, LITTLE KIDDIES, WHAT DO YOU THINK PETER RABBIT ANSWERED?"

STARTED ON HIS CAREER

WHY NOT?

URSULA: IS MY NOSE SHINY, DEARIE?
LAMBERT: NO, BUT YOUR RIGHT KNEE IS DUSTY.

THE INFERIORITY COMPLEX
(Magnified One Thousand Times)

The Inferiority Complex; Always Wants to Crawl Under Something. Unless Pushed, It Seldom Moves. If Bitten, a Victim Can Secure Relief by Reading Such Books as "Your Dormant Powers," "The Triumphant Ego" and "The Joyous Leap to Success"

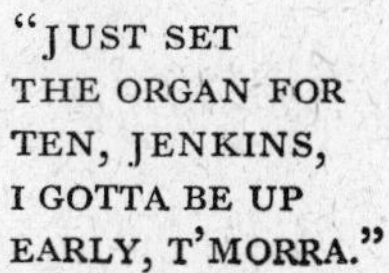

"JUST SET THE ORGAN FOR TEN, JENKINS, I GOTTA BE UP EARLY, T'MORRA."

"Oh Goody! Douglas Fairbanks is showing tonight at the Teatro Romano."

"Gawd help anybody that spits on the flag today."

LONG ISLAND NIGHTS

"Don't you simply adore the peasantry?"

ABERCROMBIE & FITCH BREAK IN A NEW CLERK

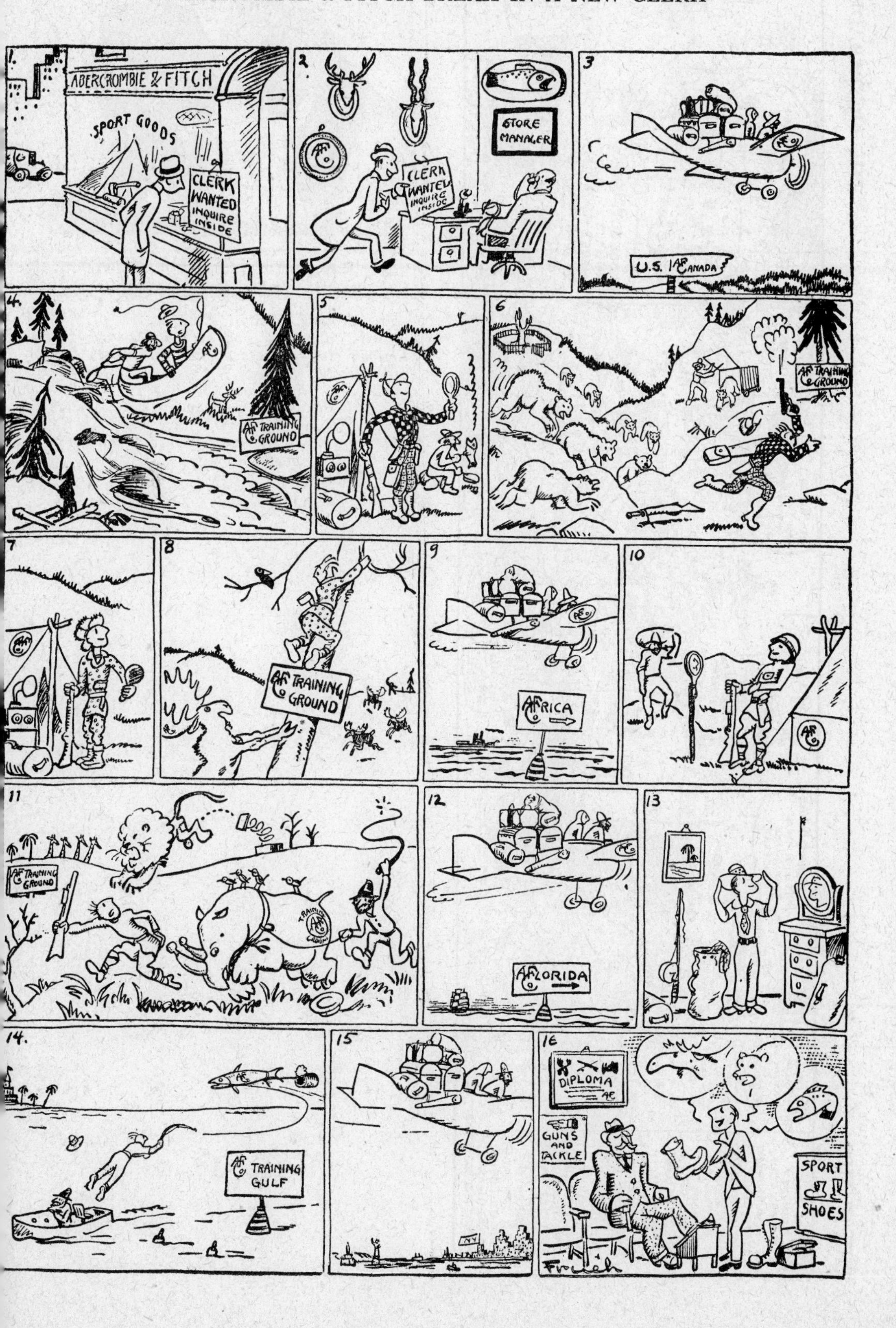

THE GUMPS — THE BIG PARADE

QUICK, WATSON, THE NEEDLE, MUTTERED HOLMES IN A WHISPER

There have always been a lot of "Wise Crashers" down in good old Far Rockaway, but Sherlock Holmes (age twelve, 174 Beach Boulevard) is the "Wisest." Said he to a friend recently, "I hit father with my car the other day." "Well, father was getting on," rejoined the boy friend. "I know," shot back Sherlock, "but I crumpled the mudguard!" Wasn't that a honey of a reply?

THE FRESH PAINT COMPLEX

An Elephant Never Forgets

Courtesy *The New Yorker*

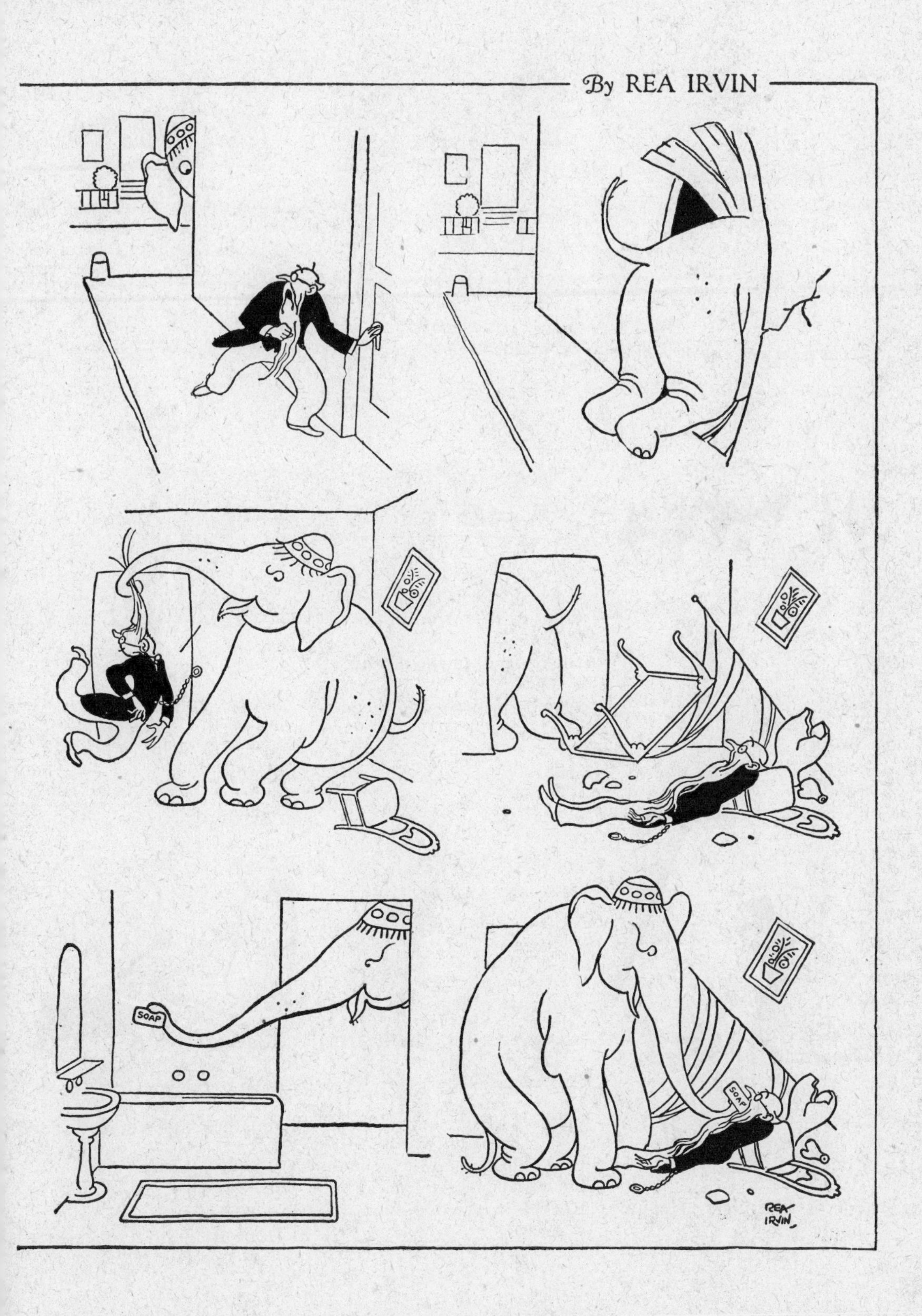
By REA IRVIN
SOAP
SOAP
REA IRVIN

HIAWATTA

WITT NO ODDER POEMS

BY

MILT GROSS

ILLUSTRATED BY THE AUTHOR

On de shurrs from Geetchy Goony,
Stoot a tipee witt a weegwom
Frontage feefty fitt it mashered
Hopen fireplaze — izzy payments

On de muggidge izzy payments
For one femily a weegwom
In de liss a cluzz "No cheeldren,"
Stoot a warning "Hedults honly."

Fiftin meenits from de station
From de station jost a stun's trow
Fiftin meenits like de bull flies
In de beck a two car gerredge
Gave a leff "ha ha,"
De wodder——

Smooked de Chiff a pipe tebecca
Opp it rose from smoke a wapor
Clouts from smoke de hair assended
Like by Yellowstun de Kaiser

Like a hoil-well wot it goshes
Goshes in de hedwertisements
On de coicular it goshes
Ruzz de smoke opp, high witt deezy

Grebbed de boids witt bists de gezzmesks
Flad de rebbit witt de roebock
Bonded like a strick from lightning
Grissed witt griss, a strick from lightning

Gave de bear a ronning bruddjomp
Gave de helk witt deer a high-dife
Gave a baiting beauty high-dife,

Witt de hentlers in de wodder.
Loud a yell de skonk gave: "Kamerad"
Poffed witt pented hall de critchures
Hout from bratt dey poffed witt pented

In de woots expheexiated

Smooked de Chiff de pipe tebecca
It should be de smook a tsignal
All de tripes should hev a mitting
In de forest fumigated

So de beeg Chiff gave a mitting
From de tripes it came de pipple
To de mitting — in de pow-wow
Came de Chiffs und came de Sockems

Came de skwuzz witt de cabooses
To de mitting
Grad-u-ally—
In de trizz it strimmed de brizzes
Gave a leff "ha ha" de wodder
Gave de Chiff a knock de gravel
From de mitting rad de minutes
From de lest wicks mitting minutes

How it made de Chiff a notion
Pessed witt sacunded de notion
Pessed witt wotes witt razzelutions
Pessed a sluggan "Boost Kiwanis"
Brutt befur de Board new beezness

Opp it rose Chiff Wreenkled Deesh-Pen
Hancient chiff from furr-scur weenters
Not forgatting hall de sommers
Ploss a copple spreengs witt hutums

In de weend it wafed de wheeskers
Like a proon de faze resambled
From de faze from Wreenkled Deesh-Pen
Eef it laid out in a straight line

Hend to hend would rich de wreenkles
From New Yuk to Pessadinna
Pessadinna, Kellifurrnia
Gave de Chiff a hexclamation
"Hock ye! Hock ye — nubble worriers
In de willage, in de weegwom
Wheech it stends a rule no cheeldren

Brutt lest wick de stuck a Baby
From de name from Hiawatta
Wott'll be I hesk a henswer!"
Opp it jomped de skwuw Nokomis
Spicking witt a woice axcited
"I would like to make a notion
What I should adapt de baby,"
Gave the Chiff a hexclamation
"Ho K, is by me agribble."

So it grew opp Hiawatta

Went itch day to keendergotten
Loined from all de boids a lengwidge
From de boids witt bists a lengwidge
All de critchures from de forest
He should be on spicking toims witt

Gave a hoot de howl "Goot Monnink"

Honked a honk de gooze "Hollo Keed"

Gave a scritch de higgle "Yoo Hoo"

Quecked a queck de dock "How guzzit?"

Gave a bozz de bizz "Hozz beezness?"

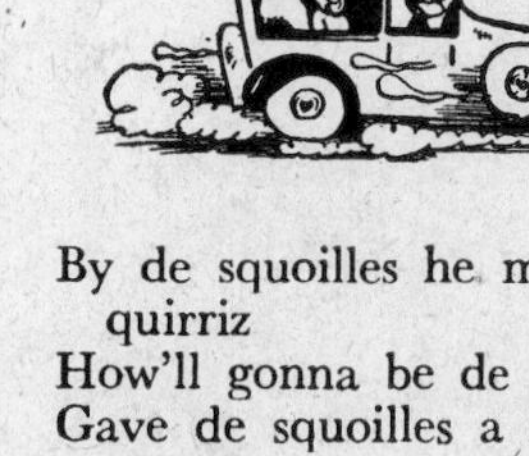

By de squoilles he made inquirriz
How'll gonna be de weenter
Gave de squoilles a henswer proutly.
"Hall de signs witt hindications
Pointing to a beezy sizzon,
Reech witt prosperous a hera,

Witt a houtlook hoptimeestic.
In de trizz we got dipositts
Wot it feegures opp a tuttle
Feefty-savan tousand hacorns
Ulso from seex tousand wallnots
Stends a Kepital witt Soiploss."

In de durr in sommer ivvnings
Set de leedle Hiawatta
Watched it geeve de strim a reeple
From de reeple saw de moon rize
In de sky it rose de moon opp
Opstess like a helewator.
Denced oppon de moon a shedow,
Esked a quashtion Hiawatta
How it got de moon de shedow
So de grendma gave a henswer,

Wance oppon a time a sousepot
From de name from Beeg-Chiff Blind Peeg,
Came hum trick lock in de monnink
Fool from jeen — from fire wodder
Fool from fire water cockite

Witt tree frands from de Spick Izzy

On itch one de heep, a heep flesk
On itch heep a hempty heep flesk
Seenging ballots tsentimental
Seng "Switt Edelline" de quottet

To de durr it came de meessus

Witt a rulling peen a beeg one
Witt a tommy-huck a hod one
Came witt a potato mesher
In de hend a coppet-bitter
In de heye a look a med one
Sad de Chiff "Boys mitt de meessus,"
"Hollo, switthott come — hic —kees us."

Witt de rulling peen she keesed him
On de cuccanot she keesed hem
On de binn oppon de buld spot
On de dome she deedn't meesed him.
"Yi yi yi. Is diss a system?"
Gave de Chiff a hexclamation
Gave a leff "ha ha" de wodder
Gave a yell de geng "Rezzbarrys."

By de Boyish Bob he grebbed her,
Hopp into de hair he trew her
On de moon full-fuss she lended
In a hipp de meessus lended
Making shedows wheech you see dere
Making Cholston jeegs witt shimmiz.
Hm—a dollink Hiawatta
Ate opp all de Hindian Corn Mill.

THE SEVEN INFALLIBLE SIGNS OF SENILITY. Diagram showing the average age at which man begins to sputter and fume about:

Modern Art	Modern Youth	Modern Books	Modern Dress	Modern Dancing	Modern Inventions	Modern Anything

I WILL NEVER ASSIST YOUR WICKED DESIGNS DEFIED THE HONEST STABLE-BOY FIRMLY

HER JAZZ-MAD MOTHER

Speaking of wild orgies, you should have seen the one I was on last week, but that is another tale. This one concerns Miss Pussy Gimblewitch, 2356 Plaza Road, Jamaica, who is a "home girl" and makes swell bean soup. Come around sometime, folks. Anyway, Pussy was out with a friend and they saw a couple cows in a field. Said the friend, "Oo, look at the pretty white cow! She's the one that gives white milk!" "Yeh," replied Pussy, peeling a banana, "in a minute I suppose you'll tell me that the brown one over there gives coffee!" The friend was so abashed that he nearly got lockjaw.

"This is the young lady I want you to meet sometime, Bill."

"Two eggs, three-minute boiled. Hurry! Only got one minute to catch my train."

"We can't have any children, you know. The management won't let us."

THE DANCE-MAD YOUNGER SET

CHICAGO COP: WHAT'VE YOU GOT IN THAT CAR?
GANGSTER: NOTHIN' BUT BOOZE, OFFICER.
COP: I BEG YOUR PARDON—I THOUGHT IT MIGHT BE HISTORY BOOKS.

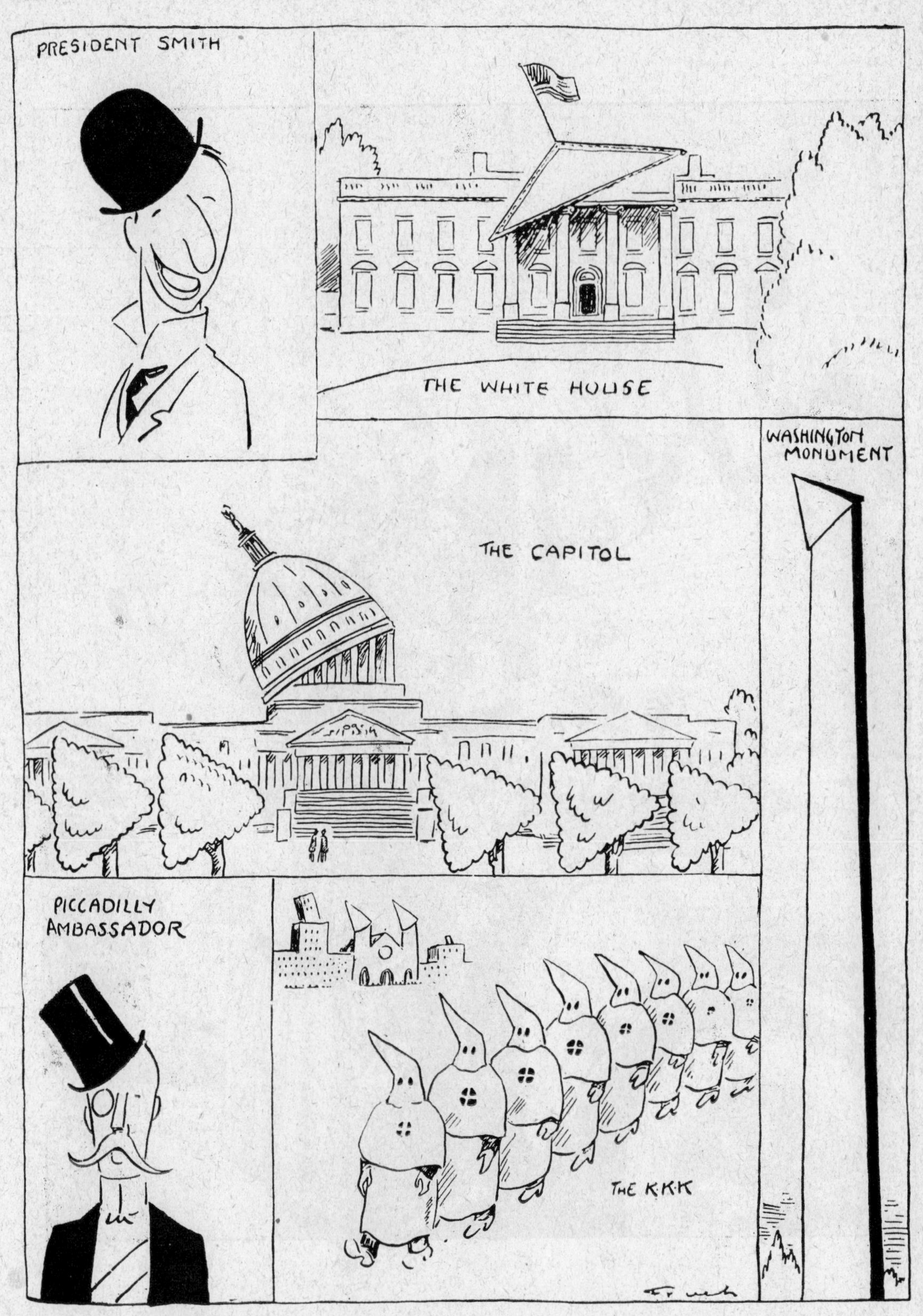

POSSIBLE INFLUENCE OF AL SMITH ON THE NATIONAL CAPITAL

THE CADET WHO HAD DRIED APPLES AND WATER FOR LUNCH

"It's broccoli, dear."
"I say it's spinach, and I say the hell with it."

POLLY AND HER PALS

"No—no inconvenience
whatsoever, Madam,
I assure you."

Money Isn't All

OUTDOOR SPORTS

ABIE THE AGENT

"Just a minute, dearie, until I shut off Herbert Hoover."

A Few for the Many

THE WAITER WHO PUT A CHECK ON THE TABLE FACE UP

INDUSTRIAL CRISES

The day a cake of soap sank at Procter & Gamble's

At the Life Insurance Agents' Banquet

CRISIS IN WASHINGTON

Mr. Coolidge refuses point blank to vacate the White House until his other rubber is found.

"But don't you understand? You are a bear and you've been cornered by the bulls."

TOOTS AND CASPER

BY JIMMY MURPHY

Tad's Favorite Indoor Sports

TOOTS AND CASPER

"And these green pinheads are our field salesmen."

"Button me, big boy."

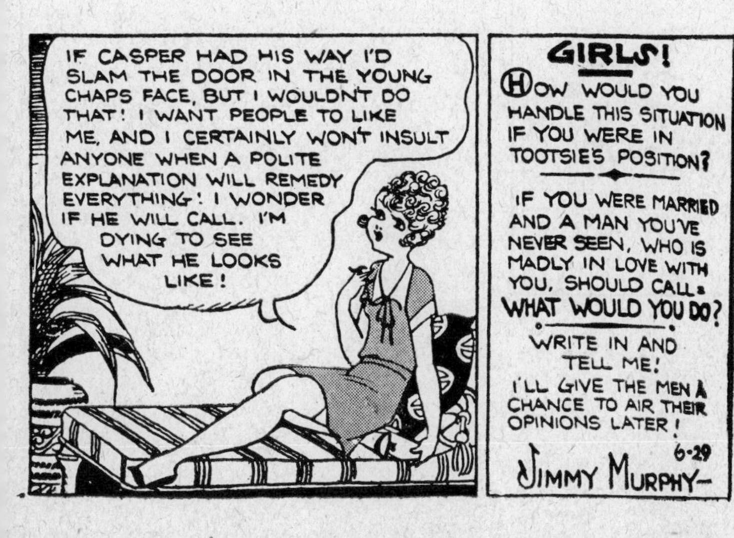

KRAZY KAT
The Reaper
Registered U. S. Patent Office.

"My dear, your skirt is positively *drag*ging!"

KRAZY KAT
Registered U. S. Patent Office.
Keeping Ignatz Square.

THE SCORE IS FORTY "LOVE" SAID FRANK MEANINGLY

"Most of the action of my story takes place in a cemetery," an author is reported to have told a fair friend of his. "Well," said the demure girl, throwing him a roguish glance, "isn't that the best possible place for a plot?" Both of them had a good laugh at this, and linking arms, they adjourned to the bar.

"Off the lawn! Off the lawn!"

Where Is When? *Oh, Come Again*

"WATCHA GOT IN THAT BAG?"

Bang! And Then *Back in the Pen*

SUGGESTED DESIGN

Chicagoans to Build Theatre for Ziegfeld—Signs Contract for 44-story Building—To Establish Mid-West Centre for Glorification of the American Girl—NEWSPAPER HEADLINE

". . . 'But your body—your fair white body—belongs to me,' hissed Rudolph."

"Gad! My wife looks terrible tonight."

"Sir! You are speaking of the woman I love."

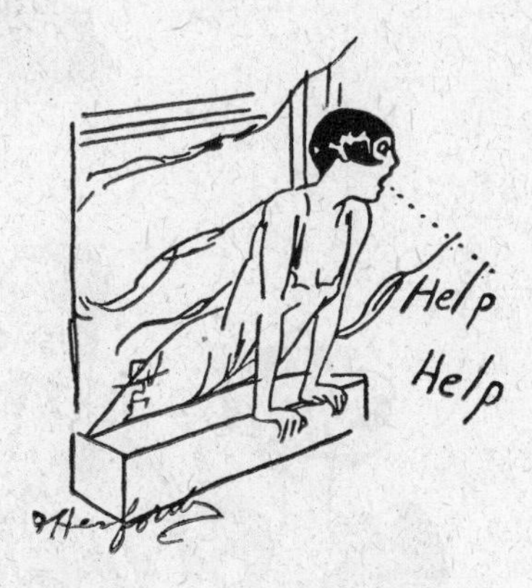

"And did you have a nice time on your honeymoon?"

"Oh, wonderful! And I met the darlingest man."

"—and I consider your conduct unethical and lousy."

"You're so kind to me, and I'm so tired of it all!"

"Boo! You pretty creature!"

"We want to report a stolen car."

THE VERY LAST WORD in motor cars. Detroit manufacturer produces an automobile that is so low and smart that a human being can't get into it at all.

"My Gawd, don't your kind never eat?"

THE CHAMPION OF CHAMPIONS

"Wilbur! You've *got* to see Santa Claus!"

*"Good Gracious, Mrs. Snitkin!
Startin' a Farm?"*

"CRIPES! LOOK AT THE SHOULDERS ON THEM GUYS."

WHEN IT WASN'T GOOD JUDGMENT TO TRY ANYTHING NEW.

"AS OTHERS SEE US"

AS WE LOOK TO THOSE WHO ARE WASTING THEIR EFFORTS IN TRYING TO REFORM US

TO THE BOY OF TWELVE WE SEEM SO OLD THAT WE CREAK

SOME WIVES SEE THEIR HUSBANDS ONLY AS MONEY MAKING MACHINES

TO THE EARNEST PERSON WHO IS "*DOING* SOMETHING IN THE WORLD" WE SEEM TO BE JUST A SHIFTLESS LAZY, GOOD FOR NOTHING TRAMP

THE TRAFFIC COP'S IDEA OF US

METROPOLITAN MOVIES

"I'm the little girl that lives across the hall and my mother wants to know if she can borrow a cup of gin and two oranges until tomorrow."

"Yes, I know the piano needs tuning, but for my Rosie's playing it don't make any difference."

"That's funny, I thought I put the dill pickles inside the tennis shoe."

"He said he'd take me out in his car and give me golf lessons, and he brings me in a pee-wee car to a Tom Thumb course."

Today the stenographer is a "private secretary" and she is radiant with Joy, Jazz and Juniper.

HAROLD TEEN

Wall Street Joys and Glooms  By T. E. Powers

WANTED—MEN OF IRON

"If you get me outta this criminal-assault charge, I can t'row a lot o' business your way."

"With you I've known peace, Lida, and now you say you're going crazy."

"Get Mama a needle and thread like a good boy, and don't stand there gaping!"

"It's only a wild guess, but I'd say this end goes on that end over there."

HAROLD TEEN

"How's de show, Mike—any new ideas we kin use?"

"That's the original shoestring I started on."

POP BRINGS 'EM BACK TO EARTH

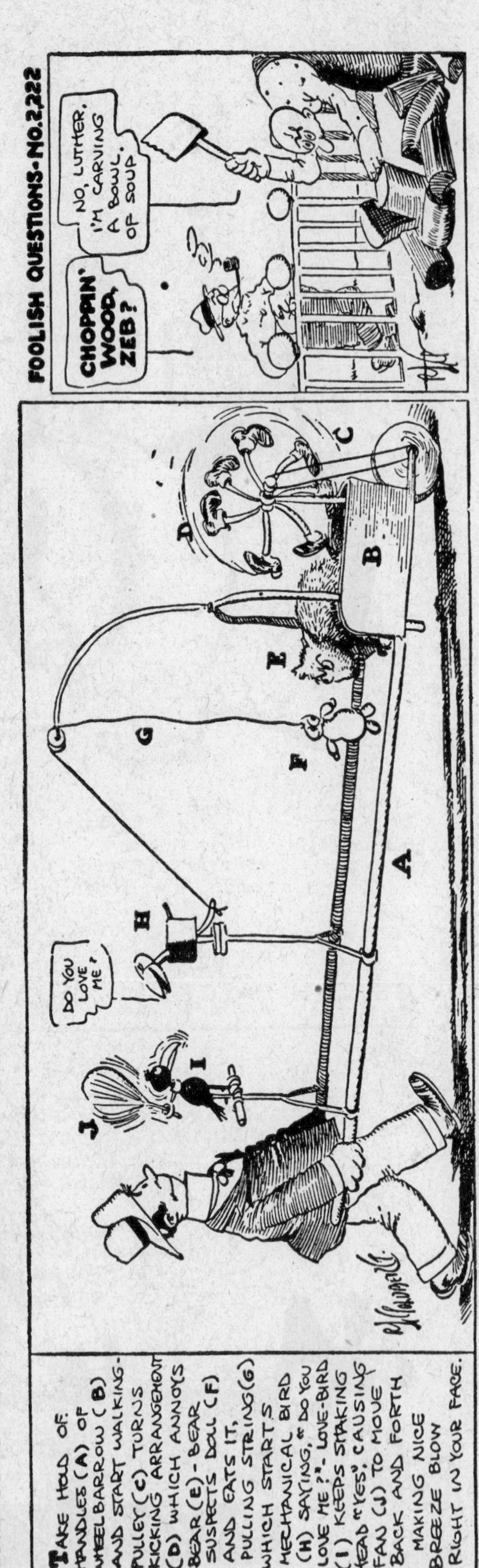

GET ONE OF OUR PATENT FANS AND KEEP COOL

THE MAN WHO STARTED THE DAY by reading a tabloid newspaper contemplates the beauties of life.

ADDED TO THE TROUBLES OF KINGS is the great difficulty of keeping awake on these tottering thrones.

"Don't look now, but isn't that a porpoise over there?"

Exclusive Snapshot of Mr. Jack ("Legs") Diamond, as good as new, leaving the Albany General Hospital

"You know damn well what I want for Christmas! I told you last Saturday at Loeser's."

"Avez-vous 'Ulysses'?"

LIFE'S DARKEST MOMENT

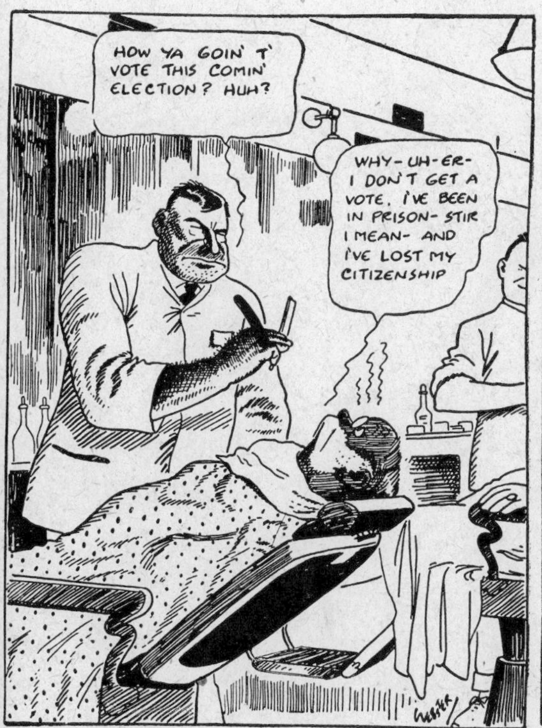

THE TIMID SOUL

Higher Education—and the advanced mathematics of the rolling bones

"I had a long chat with my barber today — he says business is going to pick up pretty soon."

"Goodness, I didn't think they wore those things any more."

"There is also another very grave question for us to decide: what shall we do with Germany?"

"I don't know. George got it somewhere."

"Be on your toes this afternoon, Miss Adams. I expect a telephone call."

"Now promise me you'll keep an eye on my little girl."

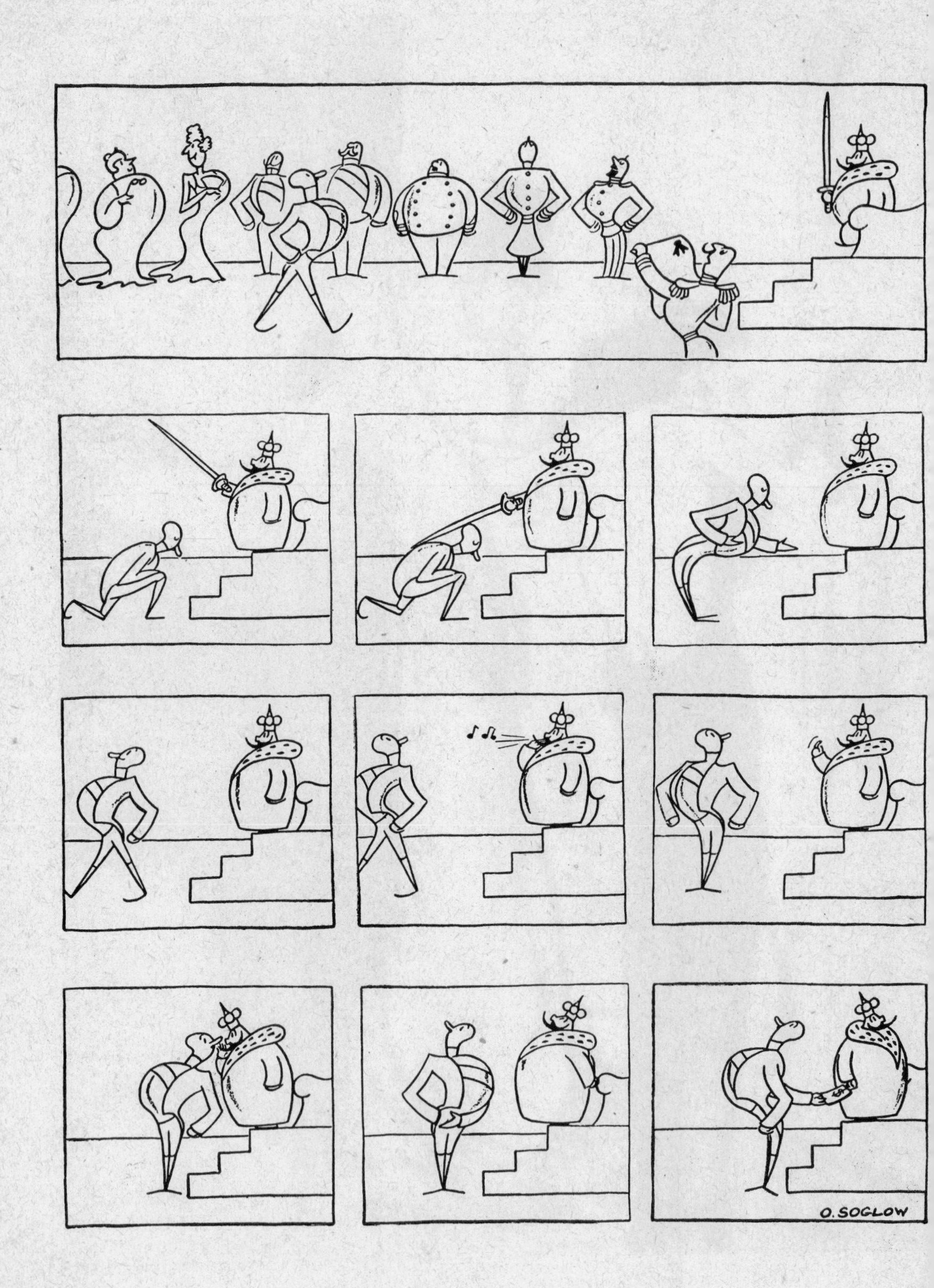
O. SOGLOW

"You and your horsie get away from me and stay away!"

"We are going to hear from one who has sinned greatly."

"I feel like God!"

"All right, have it your way—you heard a seal bark!"

THE HOUND AND THE BUG

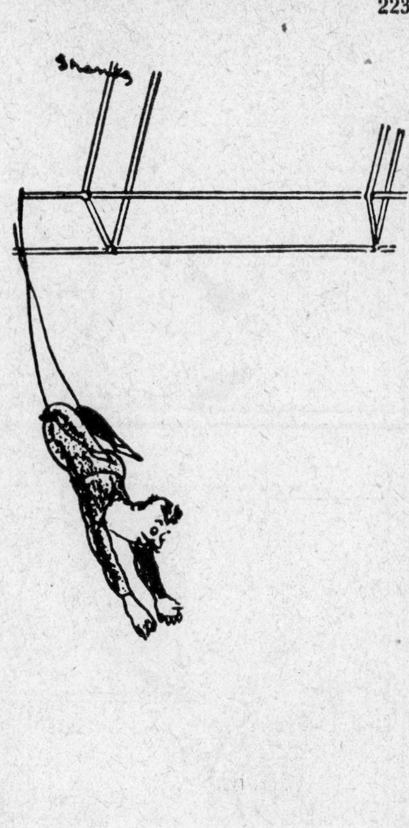

"Oop—sorry."

INVENTIONS OF PROFESSOR LUCIFER BUTTS

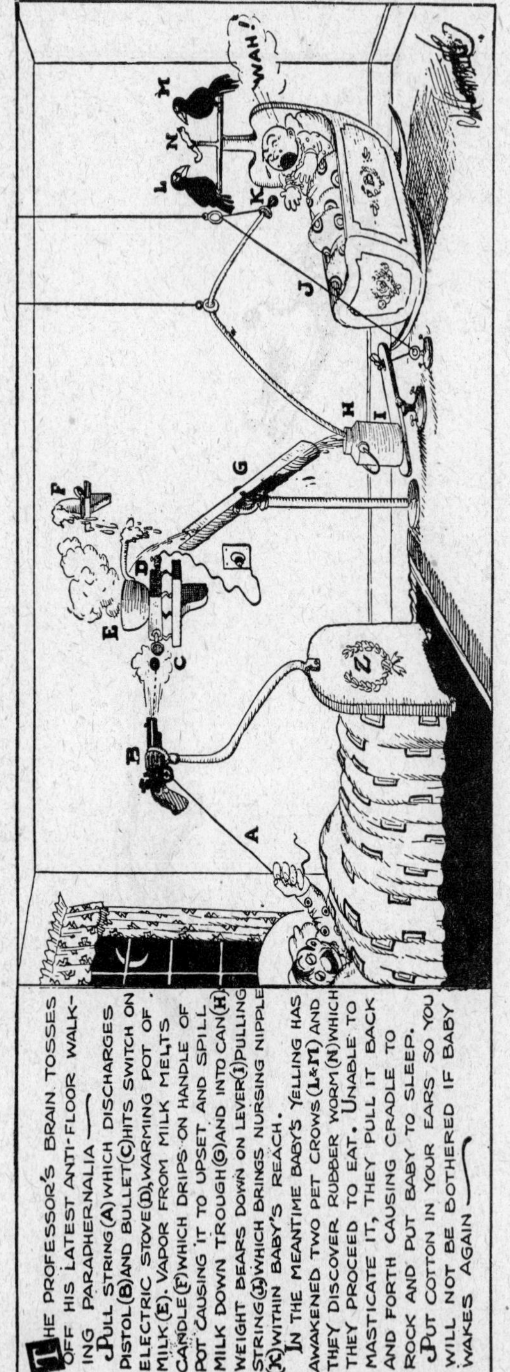

PROFESSOR BUTTS STEPS INTO AN OPEN ELEVATOR SHAFT AND WHEN HE LANDS AT THE BOTTOM HE FINDS A SIMPLE ORANGE SQUEEZING MACHINE. MILK MAN TAKES EMPTY MILK BOTTLE (A) PULLING STRING (B) WHICH CAUSES SWORD (C) TO SEVER CORD (D) AND ALLOW GUILLOTINE BLADE (E) TO DROP AND CUT ROPE (F) WHICH RELEASES BATTERING RAM (G). RAM BUMPS AGAINST OPEN DOOR (H) CAUSING IT TO CLOSE. GRASS SICKLE (I) CUTS A SLICE OFF END OF ORANGE (J) AT THE SAME TIME SPIKE (K) STABS "PRUNE HAWK" (L) HE OPENS HIS MOUTH TO YELL IN AGONY, THEREBY RELEASING PRUNE AND ALLOWING DIVER'S BOOT (M) TO DROP AND STEP ON SLEEPING OCTOPUS (N). OCTOPUS AWAKENS IN A RAGE AND SEEING DIVER'S FACE WHICH IS PAINTED ON ORANGE, ATTACKS IT AND CRUSHES IT WITH TENTACLES, THEREBY CAUSING ALL THE JUICE IN THE ORANGE TO RUN INTO GLASS (O).
LATER ON YOU CAN USE THE LOG TO BUILD A LOG CABIN WHERE YOU CAN RAISE YOUR SON TO BE PRESIDENT LIKE ABRAHAM LINCOLN.

"Are you the young man that bit my daughter?"

"Before showing you these reproductions of great paintings posed by living models, I must request you there be no cheering or whistling."

"Doesn't he make a marvellous Coolidge?"
"S-h-h-h! He is Coolidge."

"Six weeks is a long time, Abdul, without seeing a woman!"

"Touché!"

"The father belonged to some people who were driving through in a Packard."

IMPOSSIBLE INTERVIEW
John D. Rockefeller versus Josef Stalin

DEMOCRACY

PART THREE

The New Deal

THE NEW DEAL put the high-brow artists on the spot. For the first time in history, the Federal government granted subsidies, jobs, and relief to artists, and the high-brows, not without influence, received many of the choicest commissions. Their failures were instant and monumental. Obliged by the articles of the awards to deal with American subject matter—social progress, local customs, and the like—they could not of a sudden make the readjustment, and hence covered public walls with exotic travesties of art. The only creditable projects were those executed by men selected from a growing school of Americans who painted from their direct experiences in native environments.

Such futility of effort could not be urged against the work of the cartoonists and humorists. The only adjustment they had to make was to pay more taxes as their incomes mounted to the higher brackets. One time, in a give-and-take with Walt Disney, that eminent American warned me that if I should ever call him an artist or discuss his pictures in the language of art, he would forever deny me the privilege of reproducing his drawings. But I think that neither he nor the other good and useful men working in the field of comedy will resent it, if I make a point in their favor. Their work has this in common with art—any art, all art, high or low; it is the natural outgrowth of a living culture; as native to the U.S.A. as corn liquor and Coca-Cola, just as Italian art was as native to the peninsula as red wine and spaghetti. These comic artists, or workmen, are the best-adjusted Americans I know of—they have to be, their bread and butter depends on it. They may live in Chicago or California, or in Great Neck, Long Island, the home of the lamented Tad, of Chic Young and his *Blondie,* of Rae Van Buren, who draws *Abbie an' Slats,* and Fred Nehe with his cradle of *Us Moderns.*

But wherever they may be, they are livin and liking it, not trying day and night, in a ivory tower, to orient themselves. They are o good terms with life, participating in the mult farious activities of their countrymen, good bad, and ridiculous, and if any of them ha been taken in by the phony elements of ou civilization, I have yet to meet him. The know what makes the wheels tick; understan whims and achievements and play upon the imaginatively, concluding their strips with large and obvious moral for the benefit o everybody, including the children. In shor our comic artists have an omnivorous intere in the American people, and that is the simp explanation of their popularity.

By editorial edict and by inclination, th comic artists avoid partisan issues, the bloo letting having been reserved for the politic cartoonists. If the funny men of the stri should undertake the political panning, th results might well be calamitous, inasmuch many of the strips are circulated by hundre of newspapers. Recently, Harold Gray, pe petrator of *Little Orphan Annie,* and a roc ribbed Republican, in violation of the rules his syndicate smuggled into his strips, in th guise of entertainment, a number of nas cracks against gasoline rationing. But his tra gressions soon caught up with him. *Little O phan Annie* appears in 345 newspapers—to daily circulation about 16,000,000 — and Democratic editor, smelling subversive prop ganda, examined the advance proofs of t strip, and threw the *Little Orphan* into t garbage can. Other editors would have more of her; the advance strips were recalle and Gray, in sackcloth and ashes, was order to replace them with nonpolitical matter, pr erably humorous — not a small order.

Our painters and exhibiting artists, absorbed in the difficulties of their craft, have seldom been free to cultivate the field of humor, but a few exceptions should be noted. William Gropper, satirical painter, and a fearless battler against Japanese duplicity, has a genuine comic gift which is displayed trenchantly in his cartoons and with unchecked extravagance in his illustrations for books. The humor of Adolf Dehn, one of our best water-colorists, is expressed occasionally in satirical lithographs of metropolitan scenes; and Don Freeman, newspaper artist and sole contributor to his small magazine, *Newsstand*, has made a name for himself as a merry chronicler of New York life. Freeman's fine, clean humor shines out to full advantage in his illustrations for Saroyan's *The Human Comedy.*

Miguel Covarrubias, born in Mexico, won fame in this country as a youth by his caricatures, some of which are sharp characterizations in the modernist style, others elaborately pictorial. Alan Dunn, a first-rate lithographer, nearly always manages to hit upon a funny circumstance in the urban scene, and to hold it up to laughter. Reginald Marsh, one of America's most distinguished draftsmen, is the artist of the humbler forms of New York life —the amusements of Fourteenth Street, the Bowery, the burlesque theaters, the shops and public beaches.

Can you imagine the happy combination of artist and professional humorist, a man of intelligence and compassion, with a style of his own and a basic sense of comedy? Can you feature him, as they say in the Middle West? Let me introduce you to Denys Wortman, the creator of *Metropolitan Movies.* The world has twice changed and wars have been fought since Wortman first began to portray the picturesque tawdriness and sentimental economics of the metropolis, but his sense of humor has endured as solid as bricks. *Mrs. Rumpel's Rooming House, In and Out of the Red with Sam,* the recreations and sordid glamour of the sweatshop girls—you know them by heart, and so do Americans everywhere. And that shiftless pair, *Mopey Dick and the Duke,* two characters as native as Mark Twain's King and the Duke—they are in step with the American comic procession; for all of us love a tramp, and they are the most convincing and original tramps in latter-day humor. Wortman is every inch an artist and is satisfied with nothing but his best. He portrays the people of the shabby brownstone houses and the back avenues, not with condescension, not by force of habit, but with the warmth of human understanding.

In the early years of the great economic blight, the pessimism of the nation was somewhat relaxed by *Ballyhoo,* a low-comedy magazine devoted, insofar as it had any visible policy, to the vast absurdities of high-pressure advertising. The coarseness of *Ballyhoo,* but not the ridiculing of sales promoters, was continued by *Esquire,* "the magazine for men." *Esquire* has contributed freely to American humor, exploiting ribaldry and sex to the printable limit, and depending on pin-up nudity to ravish the adolescent eye. Its most original humor is to be found in the drawings of hillbillies—synthetic hillbillies, to be sure, but related to a humorous tradition heretofore neglected by artists. The worst of *Esquire* is its monotonous succession of off-color jokes—illustrated versions, often cleverly drawn, of stale toilet-room anecdotes.

The reformation of the thirties carried the New Deal into every form of endeavor except the making of humor. *The New Yorker* held itself together, played its trump cards advisedly, drew new jokers from the bottom of the pack, and won the stakes. Barbara Shermund's man-hunting dumbbells appeared only at their funniest—when the girls were on the loose they went over to *Esquire*; Whitney Darrow, Jr., the utility man, could be depended on to get the humor out of anyone's gag; Steinberg, with his modernist technique and his subtle fantasies, was slowly coming into notice, and Alain was a rising star. Alain, in one respect, was in advance of the others. No matter what subject he tackled, he acquitted himself with the greatest of ease, and with an impassive urbanity that was more Continental than American. But the man who set the standard of pictorial humor, the man who, from the foundation of *The New Yorker,* had given it the tone and smartness associated with its name, was Peter Arno.

In the first place, Arno had, or rather has, for he is still vigorously on the job, an extraordinarily individual and effective style. What appears, at first glance, to be a slam-bang assault on an idea is actually a precisely developed drawing every part of which helps to bring out the force of the title—and the titles are very funny indeed, but not by themselves.

If you care to examine the interdependence of illustration and caption, open an unfamiliar book of Arno's drawings, and cover up the printed words as you turn the pages, and see how far you will get on the road to laughter. I suggest the picture of an aquacade with bathing beauties everywhere, in the pool, in the background, and two nude charmers in the front of the scene, almost in the lap of a spectator—that queer little coot with the black mustache who turns away from the girls as if to register a complaint with an usher. Now what do you make of that? The caption reads, "I understood there was to be fireworks." The two together make the real Arno.

Arno has made two types of men famous, and though I have seen neither in New York, both are plausible, and I have no doubt of their existence. One is frustrated and unhappy, the undersize, black-mustached misfit who asks for fireworks when enveloped in physical splendor, and when confronted at a night club by girls as lovely as the Queen of Sheba, and much more exposed, turns away to distract a table guest with the remark, "I saw my first robin this morning." The other is the large, white-mustached capitalist who fondly appraises the cuties and when one of exceptional shapeliness passes by, exclaims, "By Jove, I'd almost dip into capital for her!"

Arno has other characters, none of them taken literally from life, all caught in rather astonishing circumstances. His drawings are brilliant illustrations of the wise saws and observations, and the comic attitude, of the boys about town.

To turn from Arno's high-pitched urbanity to the subdued humor of Helen Hokinson is to turn to another page of *The New Yorker*. On this page you are invited by the artist to a meeting of the Monday Club on a spring afternoon in the year 1941. The speaker, an officer in uniform and the only man in the house, has just concluded his address and from the look of self-satisfaction in his face, you know that he has said the right thing; the chairman has risen to express the club's appreciation—she is on the plump side, with clasped hands, the wrong hat, and a beaming smile; the group of seated women awaits the tribute in benign expectancy, and you listen to the spoken words as you read the caption: "After hearing Colonel Morgan, I'm sure all of us have overcome any fear we may have had of Japan."

The woman's club is one of the bulwarks of American culture, but to Helen Hokinson it is the source of endless amusement. She is never the cat, she does not criticize, but the solemn minor functions put her in high good humor — the disputes over the propriety of lighting candles at luncheon, the report on the annual rainfall of Dutch New Guinea, and, of course, the remarks from the chair—and this humor she communicates in unostentatious drawings of great popularity.

There are four men working for *The New Yorker* who have nothing in common except the mad propensity to abolish the law of gravitation, to change the highest mammal into a paramecium, and to murder their fellow creatures by the most casual methods of torture. Their names are R. Taylor, Charles Addams, George Price, and James Thurber, and they are neither criminals nor morons, but artists with an irregular sense of humor, the zanies of the magazine. Taylor is the closest to objective facts but he is still miles away from the everyday mundane scheme of things. With the knowledge and skill of a trained artist, he converts men and women into animated effigies, or puppets, with beaks for noses, feet in the shape of slivers, and large circular eyes, half blackened. These organisms sometimes behave slightly like human beings; they hold art exhibitions and have an unquenchable thirst in barrooms decorated with scorching desert murals; they greet each other, man and woman, like escaped gorillas, ready to mate, and loll on the beaches doing nothing in particular, the craziest, gayest actors in recent comedy.

If you have a taste for sepulchral humor, Charles Addams is your man. His characters externally are the same as you and I, but what they do is not within the bounds of wholesome convention. In lighter vein, he gives you a graveyard with a couple of political thugs copying by flashlight the names on the tombstones, a vote-getting practice common to Kan sas City; or a tropical bungalow in which a young woman looks up in annoyance from her reading and admonishes her husband to "speak up and stop mumbling," the husband speaking from the inside of a python which has let itself down from the rafters. When truly happy, he sends a sinister damsel to a dark old house to borrow, please, a cup of arsenic; and when ecstatic he shows you a father standing on a pile of books under a chandelier from which a knotted rope is dangling. The man has a farewell note pinned to his pants and is in the act of putting his head in the noose, when a well-schooled Boy Scout opens the door and shouts the caption: "Hey, Pop, that's not a hangman's knot."

I always think of George Price as an artist who sticks fast to the circumstances of reality, as if he had merely sketched a commonplace event, but the event could have happened only in the mind of the humorist. He will present a man engaged in some humdrum occupation, but the man is walking upside down on the ceiling like a fly; or another man reclining, not on the bed, but in suspension a foot above it, and according to the caption, for no good reason—he has been lying there for three days! You may have seen the drawing of the traveler who inquires at the ticket window about train connections for Niagara Falls. And why? The traveler has a purpose in life which is revealed by the barrel under his arm.

Since the publication, in 1932, of *The Seal in the Bedroom and Other Predicaments,* a cult has accrued round the drawings of James Thurber. The cult is not incorporated and is open to anyone with a queer, hard-bitten sense of humor, but I am not of the brotherhood. For Thurber's writings I have nothing but admiration. They have style and humor and dig deep into the culture of the Middle West, all of which is uncommon and delightful. But his drawings chill me to the marrow. His figures look like fetuses scatched on walrus bone by an Eskimo infant prodigy in the semi-darkness of an igloo—and fetuses are not funny. But when I look at the *Battle of the Sexes,* with those sullen savage females kicking male simpletons under the table or raining blows on their cowering heads, I laugh in spite of myself.

William Steig has many imitators, some of whom should be in jail, but they do him no harm. At the call of his name, we visualize at once his drawings of the young, but his adults are almost as amusing in their own rude way. Young or old, his people are wanting in civility and the gentler emotions, and we could easily do without them, if they were not funny. In his famous *Small Fry* series, the humor is almost completely pictorial, the captions merely emphasizing the scene or incident. Thus, under the subject *Football,* he will have a number of drawings with such descriptive titles as *Warm-up, Huddle, Hero, Appeal to Authority,* and *Mascot.* Steig understands the child's mind and in representing the behavior of the young makes no mistakes; but his small fry are hard and chunky, the toughest kids and the funniest in recent American cartooning. It is not their deportment that differentiates them from other urchins; it is the sophistication in their ugly heads. They are always too old for their pants.

Gene Carr's children, and he has been drawing them since the publication of *Kid Cartoons,* in 1922, are neither tough nor worldly wise, but old-style youngsters of pathetic tenderness and whimsical humor; while Fontaine Fox's brood are incessant practical jokers. Fox is a cartoonist in a thousand. He has been sending the Toonerville Trolley to meet the trains for five and twenty years, and the old skipper is as spry as ever. His characters are not only sharply individualized like those of Dickens, but inherently humorous: the powerful Katrinka, Suitcase Simpson, Flem Proddy, the Terrible Tempered Mr. Bang, Aunt Eppie Hogg, Tomboy Taylor, and Mickey (Himself) Maguire—funny inhabitants of a funny world.

W. E. Hill won his first public in 1916, with his page of drawings, *Among Us Mortals,* retained his popularity through the intervening years, and is now a favorite of the present war generation. Hill depicts the embarrassing moments—the slip of the tongue, the *faux pas,* the unfortunate break — in the lives of the average members of society. He is satirical but not poisonous, draws in a photographic style, and contrives his humorous effects by an exact rendering of types and facial expressions. The work of Wallace Morgan, in harness since 1900, appears only occasionally these days in *The New Yorker.* Morgan is not a side-splitting humorist but an observer of the metropolitan scene and an artist of distinction. His studies of New York life are beautifully drawn and no historian of the period can afford to overlook them.

In a nation at war, we should, I suppose, be tolerant of the arts, and not least of the art of humor, but I cannot restrain my impatience with the current tendency of the comic strips. I am a propagandist for the strips; I love their wayward myths and the upstart characters conceived in a world of fable and projected into a world of laughter; and I would defend them, were defense necessary, against the attacks of any snooty obscurantist. My grievance is that the fun has gone out of them; that far too many have no other purpose than to capitalize the child's craving for excitement. I am willing to make generous allowance for the daily strips in the newspapers, now that the federal agents have requisitioned popular heroes — the modern Frank Merriwells — for deadly work against the Axis; and I am happy to acknowledge their assistance in the war effort, two strips in particular, *Joe Palooka* and *Terry*. That popular soldier of fortune, Joe Palooka, drawn by Ham Fisher, is now risking his life and his wits among the Nazis, and his continuous adventures expose in graphic terms the evils of the German regime. *Terry,* by Milton Caniff, has long been a leading adventure strip and for good reasons: it is drawn with painstaking skill and the action, though hair-raising, is always intelligently planned. Terry, the hero, has forsworn the pirates for the duration and has lent his courage to the air force in its campaign against the Japs.

The "comic" magazines plague the country like the Japanese beetle; the drugstores and emporiums are plastered with them, the nurseries filled to overflowing—*The Yellow Jacket, The Bird Man, Tuney Loons, The Human Spider, The Blood Stained Putty Knife*, and a hundred chromatic horrors. The kids buy them and love them, and if they can't buy them, they borrow or mooch them. One night, in a little settlement among the bayous of Louisiana, I watched a group of undernourished children enter the drugstore in Indian file, and make a beeline for the newsstand. Avidly, and with dirty hands, each selected a thriller from the rack, and then squatted on the floor in the corner to read. The light was dim, but they read on and on, lost in superplanetary mysteries, and, having finished, rose in a body, as by a secret signal, and went out into the night, as silently as they had entered.

I would be the last to protest against the popularity of the adventure magazines, or to suspect that such provender has a deleterious influence on the moral development of children. My wrath is discharged at the garbage publications which glut the market with their stupid, pseudo-scientific horrors, befouling the name of comedy, and extinguishing one of the oldest and most enjoyable forms of American humor. The hurtful effects of these publications extend into the newspapers where insane adventure is slowly crowding out strips which really deserve the name of comic. But the moral and educational aspects of the question need not cause us anxiety, and for the peace of mind of frightened parents, I append the conclusions arrived at by Professor George E. Hill, of Morningside College.

After years of research in the field of tried and true comic strips like *Mickey Mouse, Bringing up Father,* and *Blondie, Tailspin Tommy*, and *Tarzan*, it is the professor's conviction that:

"Most of the words used in the strips tend to help the child build up a vocabulary.

"The use of manufactured words and distortions serves the purpose of humor and adds pleasure to the reading.

"Teachers have not grasped the importance of this form of comic art.

"The strips are a part of the folk literature of our day; their ethical significance is almost immeasurable; and they offer the best ready-made material for character training now available."

That should quiet the killjoys and alarmists. But the fact remains that the term comic can be honestly applied only to a limited number of strips in operation today. Of the old stock, *The Captain and the Kids, Mutt and Jeff, Krazy Kat*, and *Bringing up Father* are immortal, with Cliff Sterrett's *Polly and Her Pals* assured of the same enviable state. The career of Polly, humor aside, for the past twenty-five years, is a permanent record of the fads and ardors of the American girl; and though she has had many rivals—Tillie, Dixie, Penny, and

Boots—she is still the queen of her class. Of the innumerable strips built on domestic vicissitudes, two are outstanding: *Blondie*, by Chic Young, and Harry Tuthill's *The Bungle Family*. The humor of *Blondie* is gay and kindly, but the Bungles are short-tempered, brick-throwing people. In both the action is intelligently sustained from day to day. The most welcome character of the new strips, and the most recent, is little *Barnaby*, by Crockett Johnson. Barnaby is a child from the wonder books, but *sui generis*, invoking his fairy godfather amid the practicalities of modern life. Here, at last, is a blending of old fable and everyday fact; and here is humor that is magical and rare.

In my reflections on the strips and comic magazines, which are to the boys of today what the dime novels were to the boys of Franklin P. Adams' generation, I never cease to grieve over the absence of a baseball hero. The national game had an inning, once, in the strips, but with Ring Lardner's celebrated goof as the principal, and young America would have none of him. The dumb player, in truth, was on his way out when Lardner wrote about him, and is now the exception. The players of today are smart and thrifty, salting away their earnings in bonds, annuities, and farms, as any manager will tell you. And the fans of today, and all the young, incipient stars, demand a hero of intelligence and stature, colorful of course, but transcendently endowed—a leader, not a goof. The importance of such an idol to the well-being of the country can hardly be overestimated; and fortunately, he is living among us, not in uniform, but active and vocal, and ripe for any artist with the wit to take him. I refer, of course, to Dizzy Dean.

I have reserved for final honors in this long venture in Americana, the work of the most famous of living humorists, or the most famous of living artists, if I may be allowed the expression. Walt Disney, as noted before, shies away from the word art, and in discussing his work confines himself to the technicalities of his medium. He makes it instantly plain that from the beginning he has struggled with the difficulties of color and animation; that his purpose, first and last, has been the production of humor; and that his achievements are the outgrowth of methods evolved from within the laboratories of the motion-picture industry.

The origins of the animated cartoon are open to controversy, but the first successful films were *Gertie, the Dinosaur*, produced by Winsor McCay in 1909, and *Little Nemo*, a comic strip animated by McCay in 1911. The new form of entertainment circulated slowly, but when color was added and a staff of experts employed to trace the drawings on celluloid, the animated cartoon became a marketable commodity. But it remained a dawdling infant, the illegitimate offspring of the movies, until Disney took hold of it and made it an art.

In 1921, he was living in Kansas City, twenty years old, an artist of no more than ordinary competence in black-and-white drawing, but already at work in the field which he was to make his own. With his brother Roy, he brought out a series of animated comedies, and then went to Hollywood to set up shop for himself. His studio prospered slowly, for he was in an uncertain and expensive business, and to eke out his income he made designs and posters for Cecil B. DeMille. Fame came to him in 1928, with the showing of the first Mickey Mouse film in New York, and since that event his career is inscribed in his pictures and the name of Walt Disney has brought the world together. It has been said that he is the only man ever to win universal fame, and that Mickey Mouse has had more honors bestowed upon him than any other character in history, real or imaginary. At the tender age of seven, Mickey was admitted to the pages of *The Encyclopaedia Britannica*, and his presence in that august abode awakened the dead and bedeviled the editors into making the *Britannica* a living institution again. Mickey was also awarded a medal by the League of Nations, but that medal he is not wearing at the moment.

As his fame increased, Disney continued to learn and to experiment, gradually mastering the mechanical intricacies of the business, plowing in the profits in order to enlarge his studio, and bringing to perfection the art associated with his name. His material rewards were more substantial after the appearance of *The Three Little Pigs*, one of the first of his films to be produced in technicolor; and on the success of *Snow White* and other full-length feature films, he became a man of wealth and in possession of an enormous studio equipped with every device known to science, and with a corps of assistants, artists, wits, and gagmen. Never before had art found its way into the labyrinths of technology.

Disney's drawings are created of and for the motion picture, and no reproduction of them in the form of still life can give more than a faint idea of their beauty and vitality when seen on the screen. Because he knows this better than anyone else, he does not judge his drawings by the commonly accepted standards of art. He explained the difference to me in a few words. "How does an artist paint a coat?" he asked. "Well," he answered, "that depends on the artist, of course. If he is a realist, he paints the texture of the cloth, shows how the folds conform to the lines of the body, and maybe, if he is a stickler for detail, he paints in the buttons. If he is a Cézanne, he molds the garment to the flesh to make the body solid. But whatever kind of artist he may be, he gives you a piece of tailored cloth hung on the human frame. That's not the way we do it. We put a coat on a man and tell him to get going, and as he walks, we watch for indications of motion. The coat will wrinkle at the elbows and under the arms, and those wrinkles are the clues. We emphasize and repeat them from drawing to drawing, and weave the wrinkles together into a pattern to create fluidity and rhythm. Everything that we do is directed toward one end—and that end is movement. That's how we draw a coat. And incidentally, we never draw elbows or joints—they interfere with the rhythm. Everything is in a state of flux with us."

The great wonder to me is that Disney, with his humor and imagination, should also have possessed the practical mind and the patience to master the mechanics of his art. To make one of his pictures requires a giant factory and a whole community of effort—and for what? To give form and color and character to the most varied and imaginative and delicate sense of fable since Hans Christian Andersen, and the most original sense of humor since the beginnings of our graphic comedy.

"Everything that we do at the studio," he says, "conspires to the production of humor." Some of it—and the best, I think—is the half-primitive, daredevil, fabulous humor implanted in children and animals—slapstick in its sources but carried by a new medium into the land of miracles. It is no accident that his best creations are animals, for animals have long been a part of the American comic tradition. If you like him best in his more sensitive, fairy-tale moods, that is your privilege. His humor is big enough to go around.

It is fitting to conclude this book with a man who is not only a genius in the field of humor but also an artist of inestimable service to the United Nations in times of war. Walt Disney is educating the armed forces and the public by his expository films and delighting them with his humor. He is utilizing all his resources in the interest of humanity, and in the interest of laughter, which helps to stabilize the world.

"For gosh sakes, here comes Mrs. Roosevelt!"

"Nothing fazes Hockwald. He steps on all the lines."

WOLF
PROOF
CEMENT
WOLF
PROOF
PAINT
U-S-14

U-S-13

*"What's wrong wi't oatmeal,
if I ain't bein' too inquisitive?"*

LADY
WITH
MIRROR

"Soak Papa in the nose!"

DRINKERS

UNREASONABLE DRUNK

THE BLUES

ORATORICAL DRUNK

INTELLECTUAL TRYING TO ACT SOBER

THE HEADACHE

THE GALLANT DRUNK

PUGNACIOUS DRUNK

NITWIT JAG

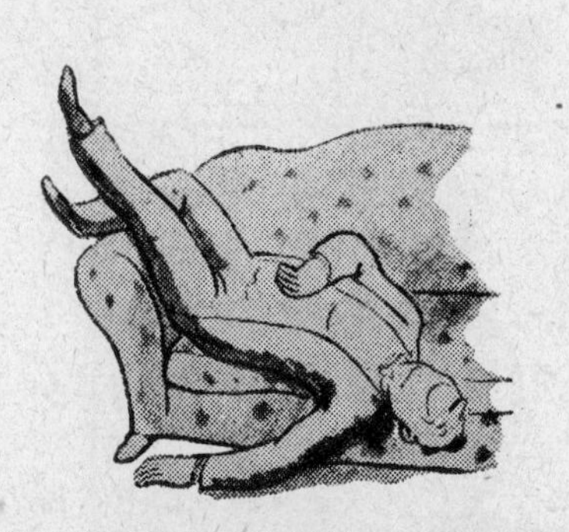

OUT LIKE A LIGHT

CENTURY OF PROGRESS—GENERAL EXHIBITS PAVILION

"That one looks like a nice, comfortable place to go in and take the **shoes** *off."*

THE PROBLEM DRUNK INSISTENT DRUNK PAIN-IN-THE-NECK DRUNK

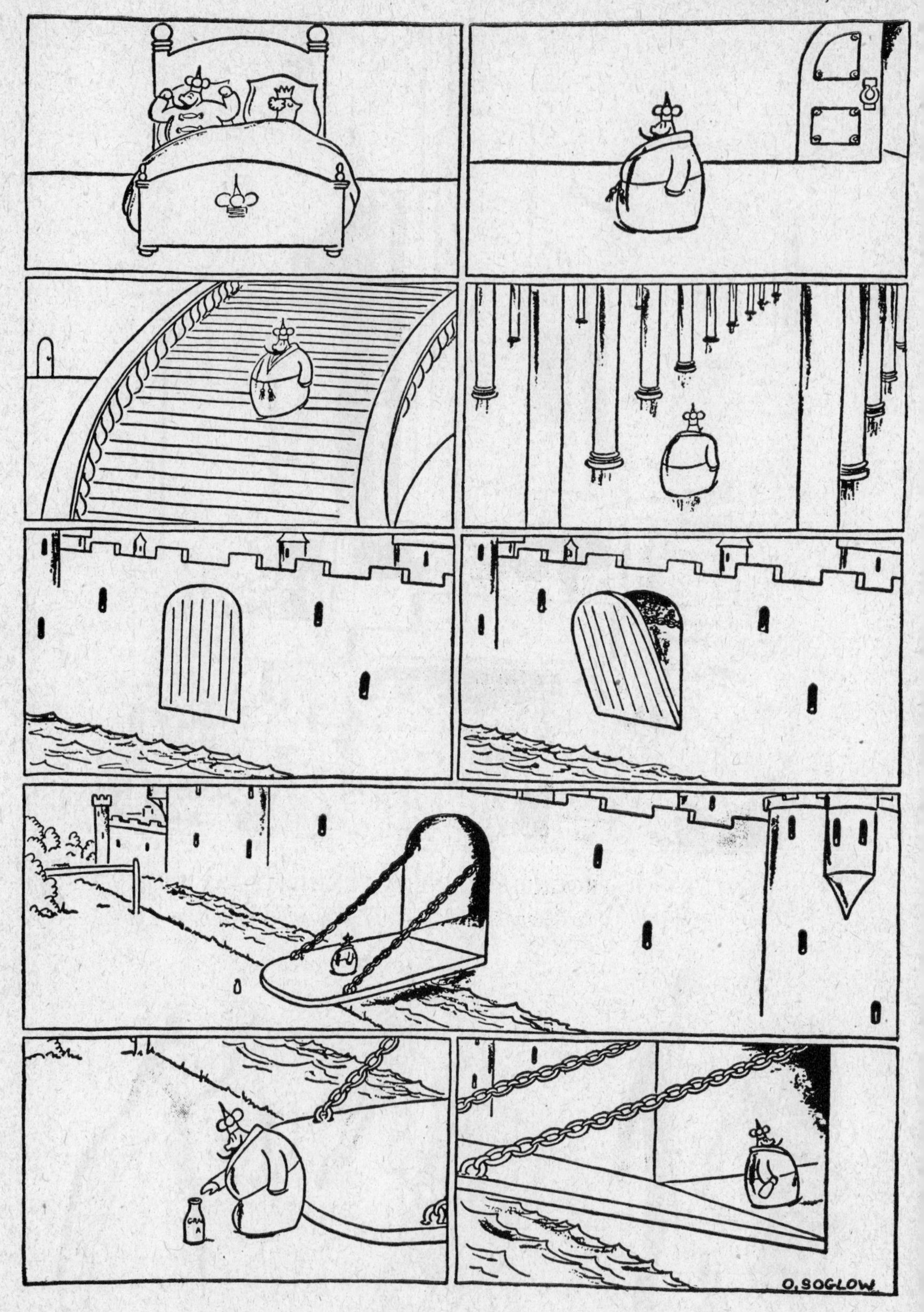
O. SOGLOW

FELLOW CITIZENS

Morning on the Midnight

"Can the American Express guarantee that I won't be sterilized while passing through Germany?"

"Are you inhaling or exhaling?"

EATERS

JACKAL

PSEUDO-CORRECT EATER

EATER, CON AMORE

STOLID EATER

UNWILLING EATER

GOURMET

BEAST

SLOW, CAREFUL MASTICATOR

"Certainly I get tired of it, but it's the only thing I know."

"What have you done with Dr. Millmoss?"

PERFECTLY CORRECT EATER

INSATIATE EATER

FURTIVE EATER

"You fellows were just being modest. You are good players, really you are."

BAH' SOMETIMES I WISH I WUZ IN JAIL WHERE I COULD ENJOY SOME FREEDOM-WHEN I LED MAGGIE TO THE ALTAR THERE MY LEADERSHIP ENDED-
5

WELL-I'VE CARRIED MANY A HOD OF BRICKS IN ME TIME SO THERE'S NO REASON WHY I CAN'T GIT AWAY WITH THAT BED-
6

PEEP-
PEEP--
PEEP!!
I HOPE HORACE HOOF-THE BLACKSMITH, HASN'T CLOSED HIS SHOP-
7

I'VE BEEN SHOEIN' HORSES NIGH ONTO THIRTY YEAR, BUT THIS THE ODDEST JOB I EVER SET FORTH TO UNDERTAKE
WELL GIT BUSY AN' TAKE IT OFF.
8

I'VE GOT TO HAND IT TO YOU. JIGGS AT LEAST YOU GOT OUT
YES-BUT HOW ARE YOU GONNA GIT BACK IN THE HOUSE?
OH: SHE'LL BE ASLEEP WHEN I COME IN-I LOCKED MY DOOR-SO SHE'LL THINK I'M SOUND ASLEEP-
9

WELL-HE GOT OUT-BUT WHEN HE COMES HOME HE'S GOING OUT AGAIN FOR THE COUNT OF TEN-HE'S AT THE DOOR NOW-
10

NOW MAGGIE LET ME EXPLAIN-
ANYTHING YOU HAVE TO EXPLAIN CAN BE-DONE WHEN YOU GET TO THE HOSPITAL-
11

I'M GLAD I BROUGHT THE FOOT OF THE BED BACK WITH ME-
12
GEO McMANUS

"You'd think George and Ella would try to patch things up for the children's sake."

"For th' lova Mike, Commander, I don't even know your wife!"

"You're not supposed to smile, Mr. Leary. The jungle-man is slowly tightening his viselike grip."

"You gah dam pussy cats!"

"Jukes got a loan from the Federal Housing Commission."

"Tears, Miss La Rue, Tears! Just Imagine Your Bank Failed! Your Swimming Pool Leaks and Your New $10,000 Limousine Burned Up Last Night!"

Heywood Broun

"This is her first lynching."

"I can't get in touch with your uncle, but there's a horse here that wants to say hello."

"We have $154,729,976 due us today from foreign governments on their war debts—theoretically I suppose one of us ought to stick around."

SMALL FRY
Criminal Types

Liar

"It's About Time the United States Recognized Us!"

Peeping Tom

Cheat

Bully

Sadist

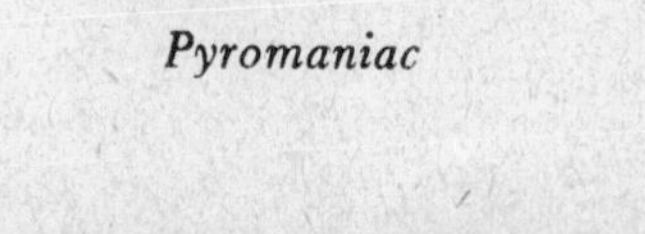

Pyromaniac

Medical Wag

Dead Pan

Self-Panicker

Alcoholic

Pearl Dropper

DISPENSERS OF WIT

Anecdote-Mutilator

Punster

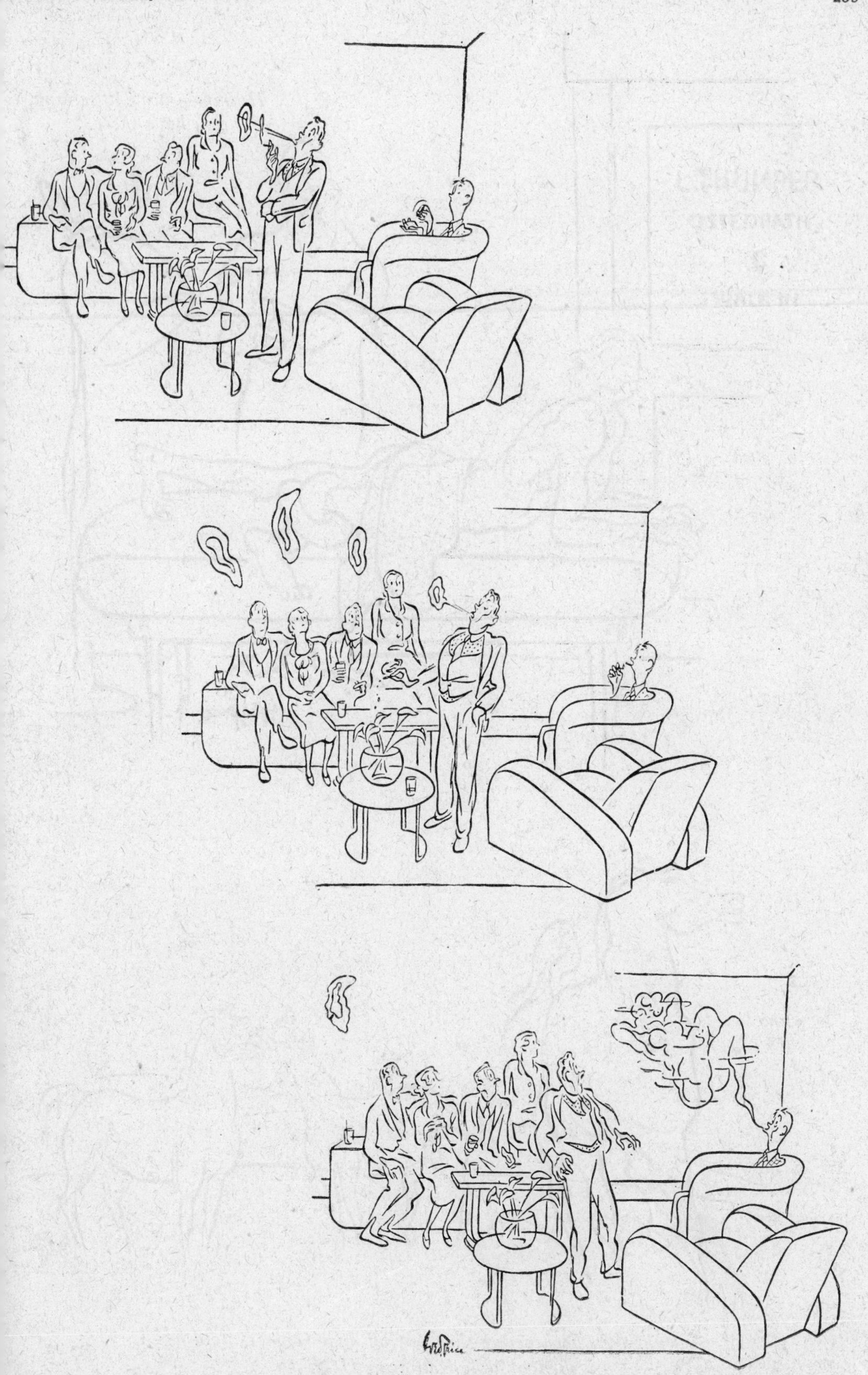

"Hmmm—nasty little kink you have there."

"Oh, she's been acting that way all day. Someone told her she looks like Katharine Hepburn."

"For God's sake, madam, where's the men's room? ! !"

THE JEST

"Let's have a pillow fight."

"If my calculations are correct, you will soon be playing third base for the Detroit Tigers."

"Oh, God! To die like this—in Brooklyn!"

"It's the best thing Nikolovitch has ever done—but he can't get himself out of it."

"Don't just stand there—get witnesses!"

"You mean we've shot the whole Battle of Gettysburg with you in it?"

"Young man!—You put that celery in a bag, where it belongs!"

"We can't let Miss Peters go. She's the only one who understands her filing system."

"There's McGuire, stunting again!"

NOT ON YOUR TINTYPE

Some more unlikely historical situations by Artist Gropper, who admits that they are impossible — but fun to think about.

Hamilton Fish, William Randolph Hearst and Matthew Woll singing the "Internationale."

Al Smith tenders the 1936 Democratic presidential nomination to Franklin Roosevelt.

Jean Harlow receives an honorary degree from Bryn Mawr.

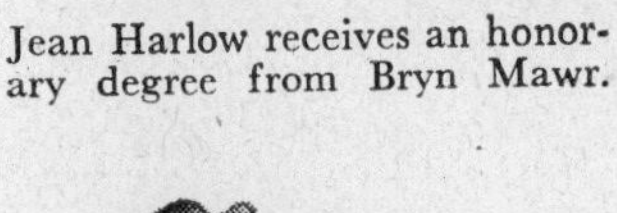

Barbara Hutton succeeds Frances Perkins as Secretary of Labor.

Samuel Untermyer attends the Olympic Games in Berlin.

ADMIRAL BYRD WINTERS IN TAHITI

HUEY LONG ENTERS A MONASTERY

J. P. MORGAN BECOMES A SOAPBOX ORATOR

JAPAN'S EMPEROR GETS THE NOBEL PEACE PRIZE

WILLIAM RANDOLPH HEARST IS
APPOINTED AMBASSADOR TO THE SOVIET

NOT ON YOUR TINTYPE

Five highly unlikely historical situations by one who is sick of the same old headlines

O. SOGLOW

"That man was ready to give up his throne for the woman he loves, and YOU won't even go down to the corner for a loaf of bread!"

"We'll have to go around the Horn. They won't take a check."

THE GUMPS

"So that's where the door is!"

A GET TOGETHER PARTY

WINNIE WINKLE, THE BREADWINNER

"Congratulations, sir. You've hit the jack pot."

Last Man Wins

ONE LITTLE KISS

By W. E. Hill

The duty kiss, showing a couple of sisters letting bygones be bygones.

The damp kisser—very unpopular with girl relatives. Particularly good looking nieces. Never lets them get away if possible.

Kissing among the intelligentsia. Once off the intellectual plane the impetuosity is terrific. Primitive forces, heavy breathing, and lamps knocked over. (This technique is much in favor with book publishers calling on lady novelists to discuss royalties.)

Cute and coy, Middle-aged bachelors get this way about kissing. Probably accounts for the old adage "Roguishness begins at forty."

The courtly kiss of the olden times, 'way back in grandma's day, when a girl wanted a man to respect her.

The maternal kiss, 99 per cent pure, used by big business men to comfort a lady in distress.

The brutal kisser. This boy in the tissue paper hat has had too much domestic champagne. In just about two seconds he is going to bite the lady on the shoulder.

The provocative. A little case, that's what she is! Has her lips all pursed up as though she were going to say "Pimlico." The young man is absolutely at bay.

The wary kisser. Stole a harmless little kiss. Thinks maybe he ought to go home. Because she's saying, "Oh, Mr. Soupmeat, how wonderful! Oh, my dear, I never knew you cared before."

POLLY AND HER PALS

A Longer Stretch of "Sun"

"Twelve, please!"

"May I see your ticket stub?"

BLONDIE

"This doesn't commit us to anything, does it?"

Meeting Him Half Way

"Sing! Sing as you have never sung before!
A Kraft Cheese talent scout is out front tonight."

"And if Roosevelt is not reëlected, perhaps even a villa in Newport, my dearest sweet."

"There! That's the kind of permanent I was telling you about."

WINNIE WINKLE, THE BREADWINNER

"Edward J. Donnely,
527 East 63rd Street.
I want a shave."

THE LINE IS DIZZY

"Are you always on the defensive like this, Miss Sharp?"

"Clotheshorse!"

"Good God, Bagby! Don't you know ANYTHING about women?"

"I told him when he started building it that they wouldn't stop for him."

"They're tied up some way with the coming revolution."

"I'm really only going in to phone."

"Oh Edgar! We've lost our baby!"

"He just bought all we had and gave them their freedom."

"Cutlets boining on the fourth floor."

"Here's the guest room. Just make yourselves at home."

"Their little minds are busy every minute."

GASOLINE ALLEY

BOY MEETS GIRL

"In the interests of science, Miss Mellish, I'm going to make a rather strange request of you."

"Armbruster here has what I think is a marvelous suggestion."

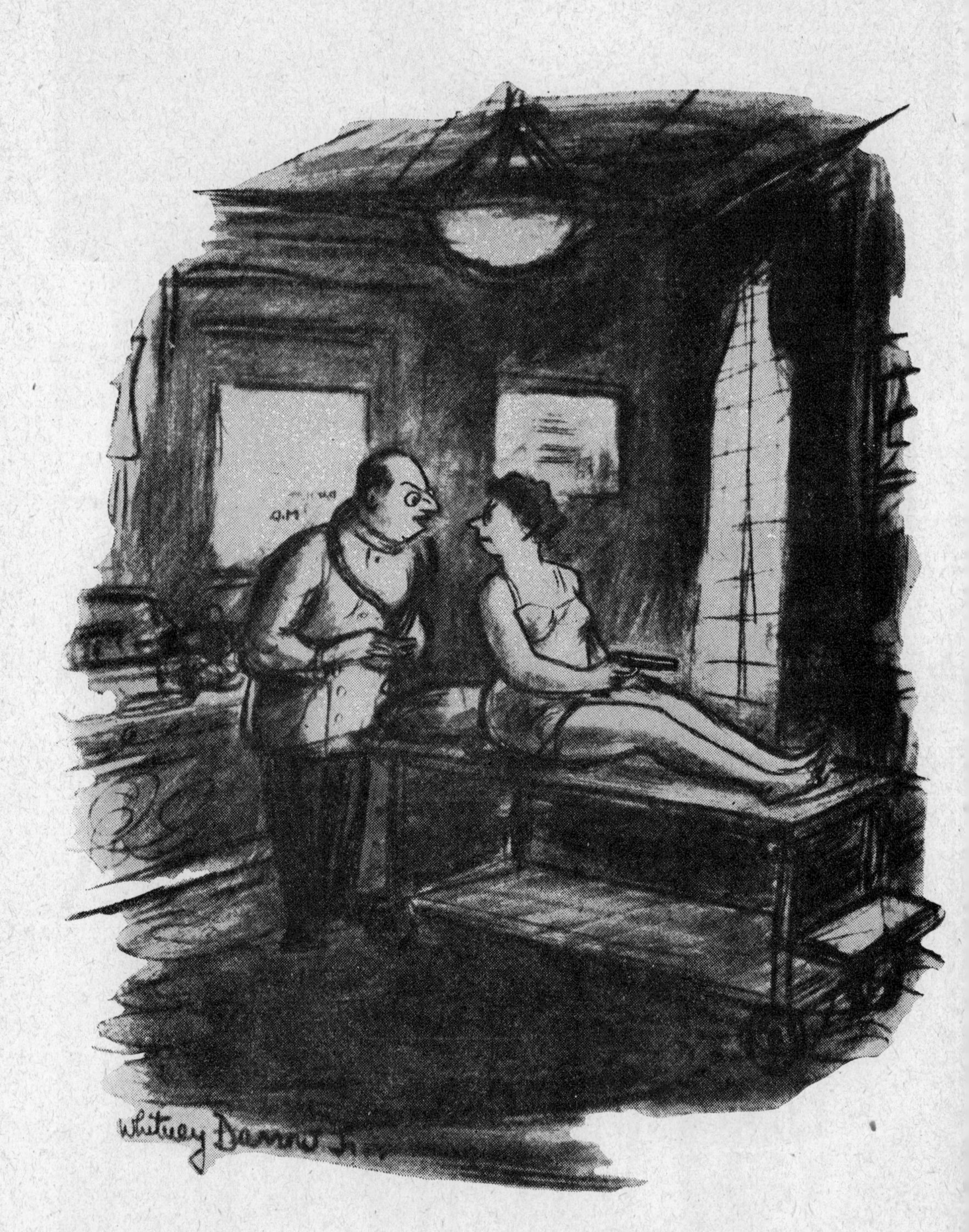

"I can't help you, Mrs. Benton, unless you give me your complete confidence."

"Well, one of us has to wave something."

"It's my own idea, sir—gives the public an idea of what it's all about, don't you think?"

MOON MULLINS

"You mean nobody took any pictures?"

PEACE WORK

"My God! I just counted five pairs of legs!"

GASOLINE ALLEY—CHANGE OF RULES

METROPOLITAN MOVIES

MOPEY DICK AND THE DUKE

"If anyone wants me, Duke, I'll be in the Grand Central waiting room until noon, the library till 5, and eating at Cafferty's free lunch counter between then and 7."

"You said a moment ago that everybody you look at seems to be a rabbit. Now just what do you mean by that, Mrs. Sprague?"

"Well, whoever he is, every time I ring up a dollar he snatches out thirty cents."

"The man is here to tune the Minipiano, Ma'am."

"Today Mr. Chatfield is going to show us a little—but not too much—of the horror in Spain."

"Keep an eye on him —I think he's got a frock full of snowballs."

"When I open my eyes, I expect you both to be gone."

"Most successful suit sale we ever had, I should say."

Mandrake Keeps the Ball Rolling

MANDRAKE THE MAGICIAN

By Lee Falk and Phil Davis

"It is unfortunate that I didn't get your case earlier, Mrs. Perkins."

"Would you mind giving us the name of that dive, Miss Hanley?"

HAROLD TEEN

AUNT PRUNY IS THE CHAPERON

"That's Kennesaw's idea for keepin' the milk cool."

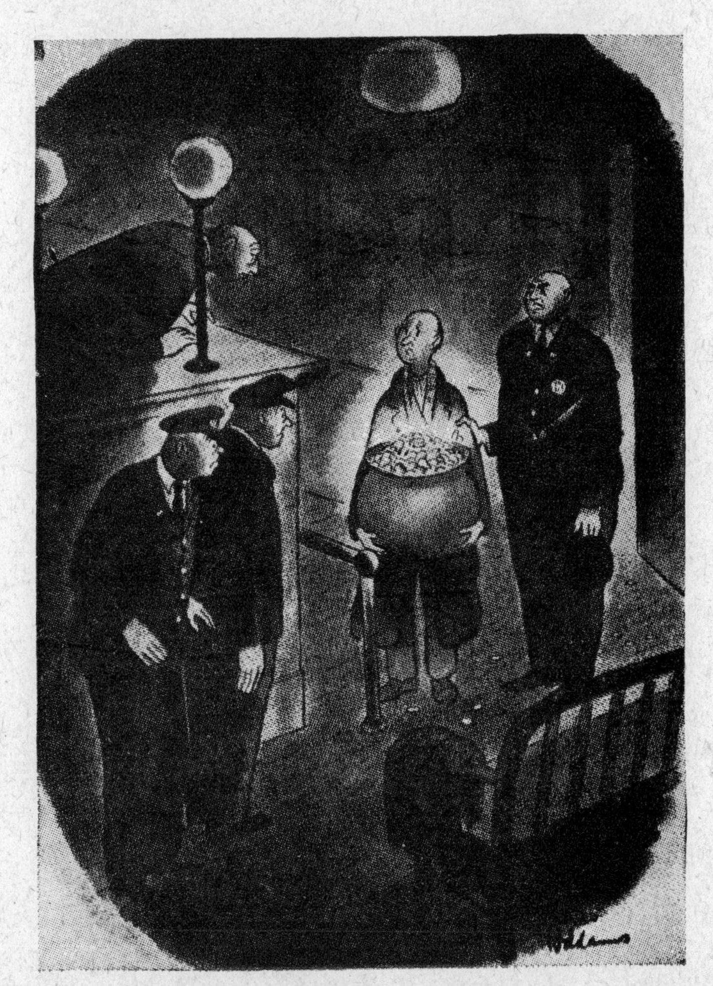

"He claims he found it at the end of a rainbow."

BRINGING UP FATHER

"Curious effect, isn't it?"

LITTLE LULU

"Hello, Momma!
We're makin' history!"

"Funny, I've been entertaining the same wild hope."

"I'm afraid as a kid star he's through."

"And how long, may I ask, have we been in drydock?"

"I told you we should have given them something for Christmas."

"We've decided to make it two hundred yards."

"Say, 'Delighted to meet you.' I'll explain later."

"Sure-footed little beasts, aren't they?"

RACONTEURS

"Here's a new one I heard downtown today —F. D. and Eleanor were going shopping, and she said, 'Franklin . . .'"

THE TOONERVILLE TROLLEY THAT MEETS ALL THE TRAINS

"How perfectly marvelous! You wouldn't sell it, I suppose?"

TOONERVILLE FOLKS

GREETINGS

Fraternal Hocus-Pocus

Matutinal

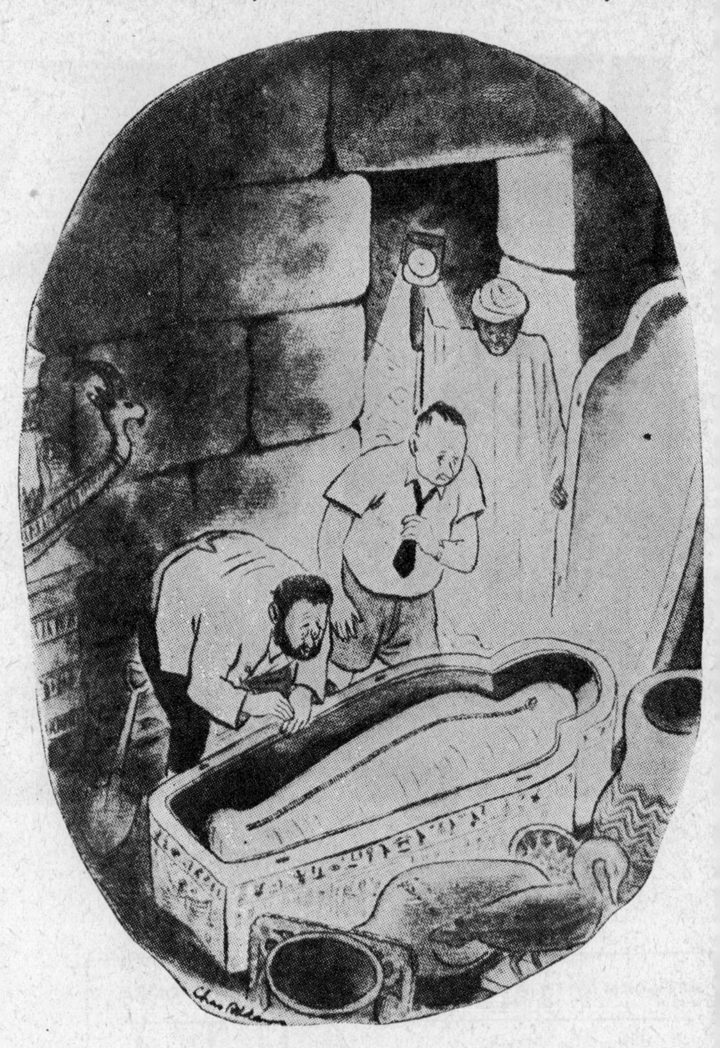

Uncertain Recognition

Gush

"Watch out, Fred! Here it comes again!"

Open Arms

Limp Hand

"A magnificent fowl, Madam. Notice how he looks you straight in the eye."

"You and your premonitions!"

"One move out of you and I'll pull the trigger!"

"You wait here and I'll bring the etchings down."

"Well, maybe you're sitting on the wrong end."

"Hinkle, was a wallet containing a ticket to Tahiti and ten thousand dollars turned in to you? Hello, where's Hinkle?"

"Well, what are you staring at?"

"Papa, do you want to see me enter a ballroom?"

"He advocates a doctrine of peaceful resignation."

"Okay, you look like a little bunny-wunny! Now stop bothering me!"

"Well—he made it!"

"Tell Hedges he's using too much grenadine, bring some more canapés—and stop trying to make Sir Hubert!"

"*Smile.*"

"Every time he gets up enough energy he starts after me."

"He's just about your size—damn it!"

"All right, boys—break it up!"

"Myrtle, I just had to see you."

1
2
APEX BUILDING
3
JOE'S
QUICK
LUNCH
4
Cafe
La
Vie
5
Special Today
CORNBEEF 25¢
AND CABBAGE
6
7
Special Today
CORNBEEF 25¢
AND CABBAGE
8
9
APEX BUILDING
10
JONES
&
COMPANY
11
SECRETARY TO
PRESIDENT
PRESIDENT
R. TAYLOR

"It's 'What?' 'Eh?' and 'How's that?' around here till I'm almost nuts."

WHO, ME?
YES, YOU !! HURRY UP AND GET ME ALL THE PAPERS ON J & B. CARSON COMPANY!

YES'R
Reg. U. S. Pat. Off.: Copyright, 1939, by Chicago Tribune-N. Y. News Syndicate, Inc.

GEE, THE BOSS IS FULL OF STEAM TODAY.. GUESS HE FEELS LIKE WORKING

HERE'S THE REST OF THE PAPERS BOSS
GOOD-NOW LISTEN TO THIS

I'M GOING TO BE MIGHTY BUSY HERE AND I DON'T WANT TO BE DISTURBED FOR THE NEXT TWO HOURS!
I WANT TO BE ALONE

TWO HOURS, YOU SAY? THAT'S FINE! O.K.
HEH HEH

I FOOLED THAT KID COMPLETELY- FIRST I PULL UP THIS BIG EASY CHAIR

THEN I GET OUT THESE HIGH POWERED GLASSES --

--AND SEE THE GAME UNDISTURBED --GOLLY THIS IS TOO GOOD TO BE TRUE
4-16

GASOLINE ALLEY

THE SHEEP SKIN

"Face the front of the car, please!"

"It's brought out twice as many for spring training as last year."

"It's from that matrimonial bureau that introduced us. They want a testimonial."

MOON MULLINS

"That's Mrs. Schuyler Post— trick photography, of course."

A COAL RECEPTION

SMALL FRY
The Lower Depths

Penny Ante

Larceny

Shakedown

Pool Sharks

Depravity

Wolves

"Pardon me, would you mind passing the ketchup?"

Nicotine

MOPEY DICK AND THE DUKE

"Gee whiz, Mopey, if y'aint pro or anti something or other, nobody wants to listen to what y'have to say any more."

"A simple 'yes' or 'no' will be sufficient, Madame."

"Hello, A. & P. We're back!"

"Whew! That certainly kept me on the edge of my seat!"

"You're mine! Do you understand? Mine! Mine!"

"Gabriel Heatter sounded an ominous note as I rounded a curve."

"Why, Harriet, I hardly recognized you!"

"Well, folks, here it is starting time! . . . One moment while we take a look at that little old schedule."

"Can't you see by now, Bernard Levin, that it's all over between us?"

"It's practically impossible to heat this damned place."

"Your wife is an elusive subject, sir."

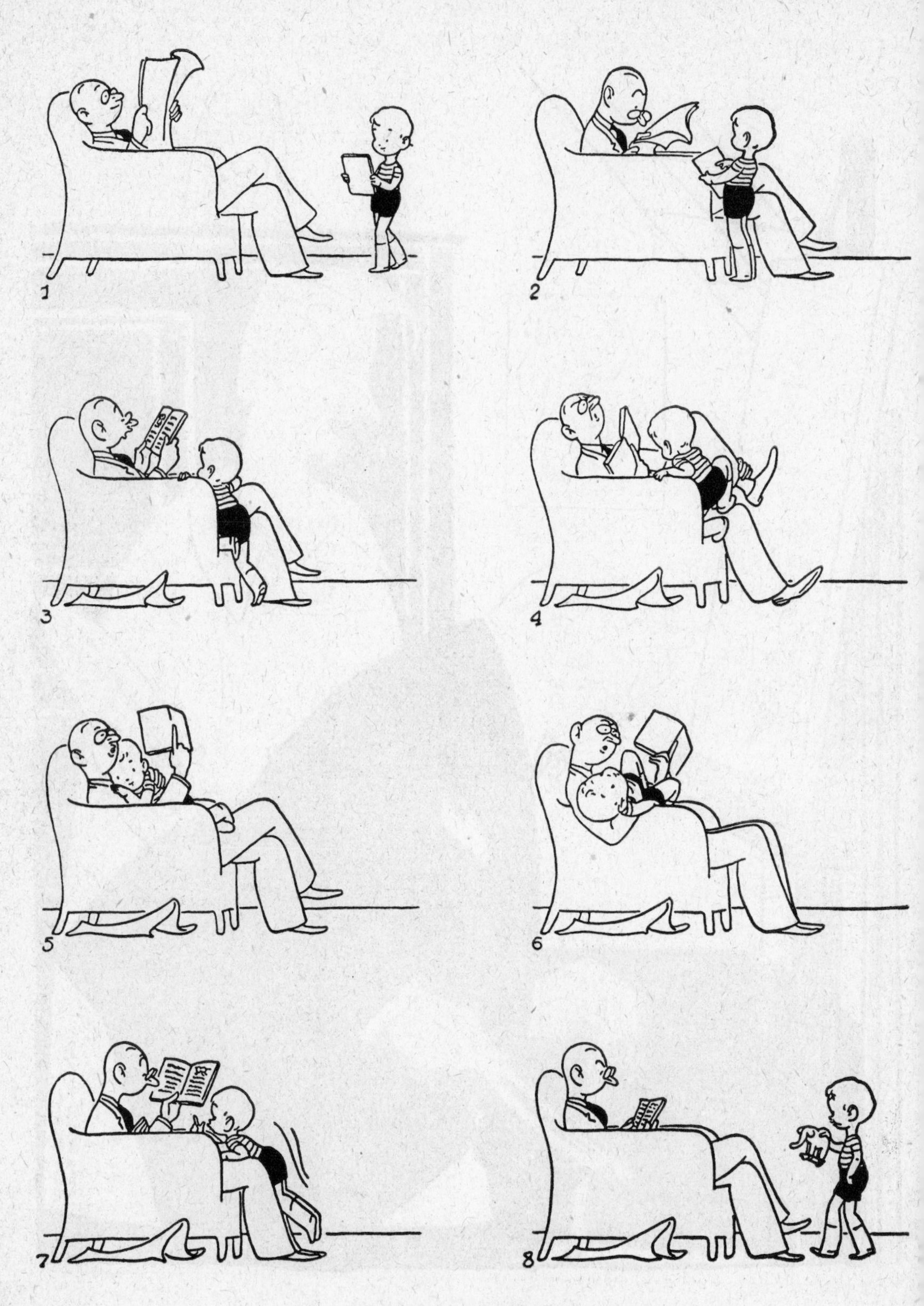

READING ALOUD (*I*)

READING ALOUD (II)

"Hmm. Have Fulton's accounts been gone over lately?"

"Ouch!"

"Colonel Bell is an old Indian fighter."

"You'll have that straightened, of course."

"Oh, if you were only here to tell us!"

"He had a very personal question, Mr. Dexter."

"One at a time, dammit, one at a time!"

"Now read me the part again where I disinherit everybody."

THE INNER MAN

Buffet Supper

ANNUAL BANQUET OF THE SANKA COFFEE COMPANY

CORN ON THE DINER (I)

CORN ON THE DINER (II)

"You'd better go now, Mother. I think I heard the warning gong."

"Now, let's see—one sashweight, one butcher's cleaver, one galvanized-iron tub, fifty feet of half-inch rope, one gunny sack, one electric torch, one pickaxe, one shovel, twenty pounds of quicklime, a box of cigars, and a beach chair."

"I beg your pardon."

"So you think I buy dames malteds for nothing!"

SNUB

"Furthermore, it can be nailed, bored, cut or sawed—just like a plastic."

GASOLINE ALLEY

"I don't care if you are her uncle—you can't see the baby now!"

Closer and Closer

"May I borrow a cup of cyanide?"

"The makers of Sun-Glo Toilet Soap bring you an entirely different type of quiz program."

"Oh, speak up, George! Stop mumbling!"

"As you know, Collins, this national-defense situation has left us a bit shorthanded. Can you ride a bicycle?"

"Come along, slaves! It's time to be exploited again."

"Oh, Oh! I wouldn't care to be in the devil's shoes this morning!"

"Sir, I suspect a spy."

"Then came the first of many little difficulties — you know how torsos are."

"C'mon, Louie. You've defended your country enough for tonight!"

"*What do you suppose can be keeping that damned pigeon?*"

"There is just one more point. Do I get my dollar now or at the end of the year?"

"Parade or no parade, you can't have it!"

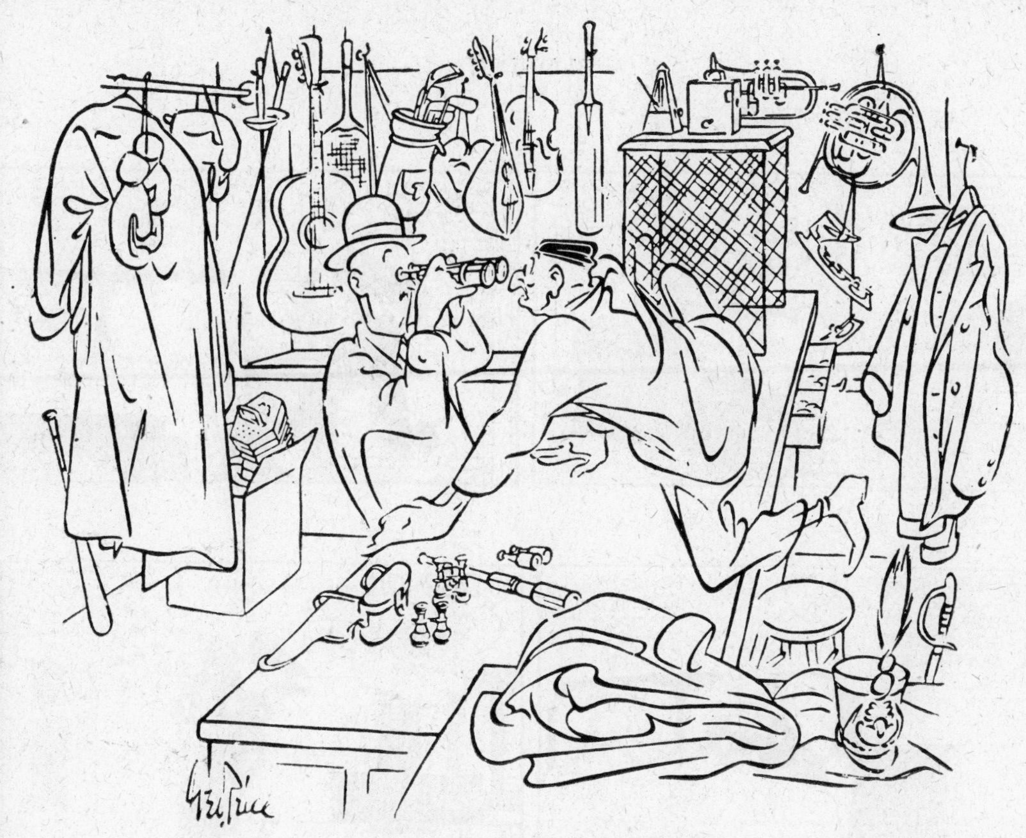

"A powerful glass, sir. Looks like I'm right on top of you, doesn't it?"

BLONDIE

I'M NOT GOING TO EAT ANYTHING TONIGHT BEFORE I GO TO BED -- IT KEEPS ME AWAKE
GOOD FOR YOU

IT'S GOING TO TAKE A LOT OF WILL POWER, BUT I'VE GOT IT
THAT SHOWS YOU HAVE A STRONG CHARACTER, DEAR

I'M SO HUNGRY I'M SHAKING LIKE A LEAF, BUT I'M NOT GOING TO EAT ANYTHING
TRY READING TO GET YOUR MIND OFF IT

BLONDIE --- WHERE'S MY MAGAZINE? I CAN'T FIND IT
SH-H--BE QUIET! YOU'LL WAKE UP THE WHOLE NEIGHBORHOOD

WHAA
SEE! YOU WOKE THE BABY! GO DOWN AND WARM HER BOTTLE OF MILK AND PUT HER BACK TO SLEEP

THAT SAUSAGE LOOKS GOOD
BUT I'M NOT GOING TO TOUCH IT

GLUB GLUB GLUB
GEE, THAT SOUNDS AWFULLY GOOD

I NEVER TOUCHED A BITE -- HOW'S THAT FOR WILL-POWER?
FINE -- NOW, BE QUIET SO I CAN GET SOME SLEEP

"We not only fill your prescriptions, sir, but we see to it that you take your first dose."

"Never mind, men. I got them on the telephone."

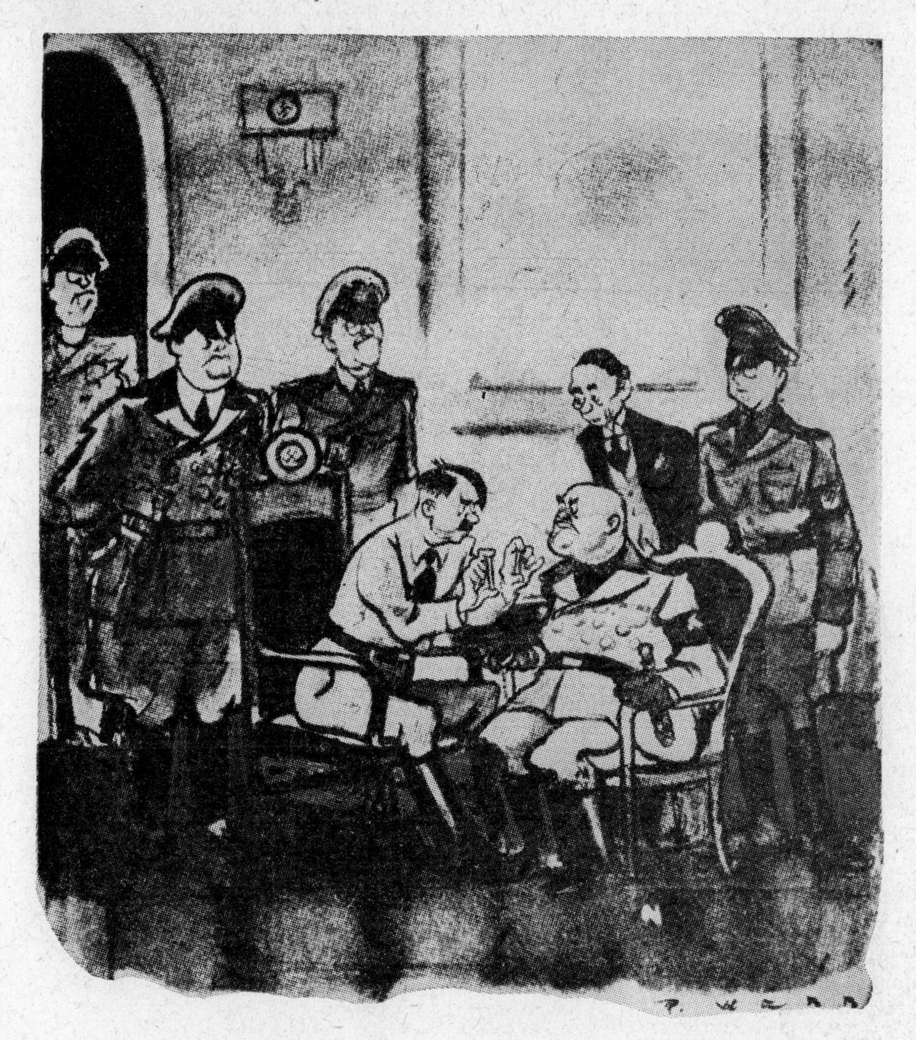

"It means something in the U. S. Army, but our agents haven't been able to find out what."

"It doesn't take much to collect a crowd in New York."

"Your being a vegetarian certainly takes a load off my mind."

"Touchy, aren't they?"

"I wuz born in 1905. Then suddenly everything went blank."

"Wait a minute, can't you? I've only got three hands."

"You have the wrong cell, Chaplain. He's just serving a short term for a traffic violation."

"Where have you been? Your plane crashed half an hour ago."

"John and I laid in a supply of things so we won't have to do any hoarding."

"And hereafter if there's anything you don't like, come to me—don't write to Mrs. Roosevelt."

"Ouch!"

"It's the 'Internationale.' If you don't know the words, just mumble."

O. SOGLOW

"Why, Stalin has a dimple! I never noticed it before."

"But, honey, I haven't got a girl in every port. I ain't BEEN in every port!"

"It's from Nelson Halliday! 'Greetings from Miami, Florida,' it says."

"You are now beginning to feel sleepy."

BARNABY

10-19
The average person's ignorance and misinformation about Leprechauns, Barnaby, is shocking . . . Of course, very little dependable data of any sort exists and no scientific field work has been done among them.
In some quarters they are believed to be the shoemakers and tradesmen of the Fairy World . . . Small business men—they're only a span high . . . But actually they're a shiftless lot.
Then again, they are alleged to possess the secret of fabulous wealth and to divulge it to the person who catches them . . . The nonsense people will believe! . . . I caught a Leprechaun years ago.
Copyright 1942 Field Publications
After I let him go, exasperated and not a farthing the richer, I discovered that my watch —
But there's one of them now! On that toadstool!
CROCKETT JOHNSON
10-20
I don't see a Leprechaun, Mr. O'Malley.
He's made himself invisible because you're here, m'boy. But he's there. Posturing on that silly mushroom . . .
No Leprechaun ever thought of sitting on a mushroom until a lady in Sussex had them do it in a kid's book . . . Now they always do it . . . Feel it's expected of them.
Like a newspaper man I knew . . . Nicest, quietest fellow you'd want to meet . . . Until he attended a performance of a play entitled "The Front Page" . . . Then—
CROCKETT JOHNSON
Pipe down, O'Malley. Ain't you never hoid about gas-rationing?
Copyright 1942 Field Publications

BARNABY

I know this Leprechaun . . . A very representative specimen named Launcelot McSnoyd . . Too bad he's made himself invisible . . Perhaps I can persuade him—
You can't make no touch around here, O'Malley.
10-21
Gosh, I would have thought that was a talking mushroom!
Say, kid! That's a poifect discription of O'Malley, ain't it! "A Talking Mushroom."
Look, McSnoyd. Let's not be impolite. I told Barnaby his Fairy Godfather could show him a Leprechaun . . . Be a good fellow and let him see you. You wouldn't disappoint the child.
Sure I would.
Copyright 1942 Field Publications
Come, m'boy. He's definitely uncooperative . . . We'll find another Leprechaun . . . Let's leave this churlish fellow . . .
But I'd like to see Mr. McSnoyd.
Who's a choilish fellow?
CROCKETT JOHNSON
That Leprechaun is following us, Mr. O'Malley. I wish he wasn't so invisible so I could see him . . .
Still woiking the Fairy Godfather racket, O'Malley.
10-22
McSnoyd, either make yourself visible or cease following us . . . I've lost patience and I'll not waste any more words on you.
You never waste no woids, O'Malley— You use them all.
CROCKETT JOHNSON
Can't YOU make him visible? . . . By waving your magic wand at him?
Of course I can, m'boy . . . But . . .
Yeah, woik your magic wand . . . Don't disappernt the child . . .
Very well, m'boy. I'll make him visible . . . And then perhaps I'll banish the disrespectful bum to the bottom of a pool or an irrigation ditch or something.
Haw, haw, haw! Now don't go over-exoiting yourself, pal.
Copyright 1942 Field Publications

BARNABY

I'm giving you just one more chance, McSnoyd. Make yourself appear or I'll make you visible against your will.
Noitz.
10-23
And then will you banish him to the bottom of a pool, Mr. O'Malley?
One thing at a time, m'boy . . . I have to refer to my Fairy Godfather's Handy Pocket Guide Don't run off, McSnoyd.
Me? And miss this?
CROCKETT JOHNSON
Well, here goes, m'boy. Your Fairy Godfather is a little bit rusty at this sort of thing—
None of them alibis, O'Malley.
Copyright 1942 Field Publications
Cushlamochree! This is very exasperating. That Leprechaun is still completely invisible.
Mr. O'Malley! Hey! Where ARE you?
Haw! HAW! HAW! Haw! Haw! HAW!

You accidently made yourself disappear, Mr. O'Malley. , Gosh!
Cushlamochree!
Haw, haw, haw!
10-24
I'll be myself again in a jiffy, m'boy, with the aid of my Fairy Godfathers' Handy Pocket Guide. Then I'll take care of that invisible Leprechaun! Just wait, McSnoyd! Where is that book, Barnaby? I can't see it .
Your book got invisible too!
Haw, haw haw, HAW! This moiders me!
This is serious, Barnaby! Come! We will repair to the quiet of your home where I can devise a way out of this predicament . . . Come, m'boy. This way. Follow me.
But I can't follow you. I can't see you!
Copyright 1942 Field Publications
I'll follow YOU then. But walk a little faster. I can still hear the braying of that vulgar Leprechaun . . . What an embarrassment! What a contretemps!
Cushlamochree, huh, Mr. O'Malley?
Haw! Haw! Haw!
CROCKETT JOHNSON

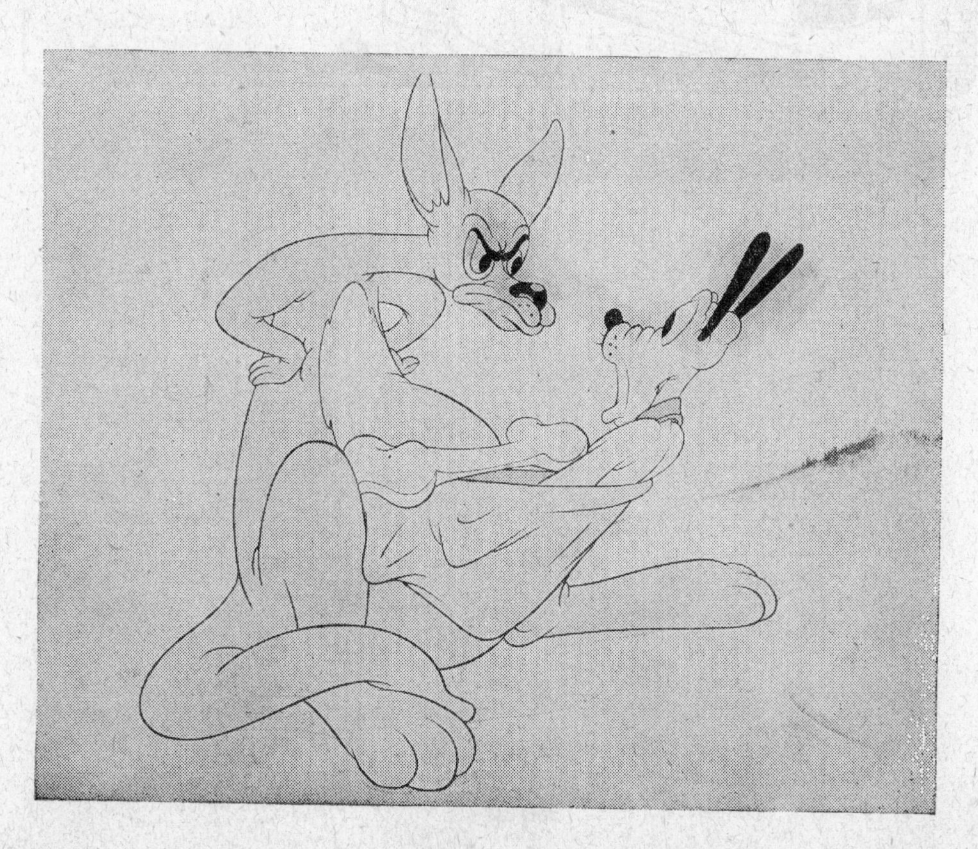

OUR BOARDING HOUSE . . . WITH . . . . MAJOR HOOPLE

"You have your choice between the Iron Cross and a suit of woollen underwear."

OUR BOARDING HOUSE . . . . . WITH . . . . . MAJOR HOOPLE

"I know it's a lot to ask, Sergeant, but would you mind throwing your arm around me in a comradely manner?"

"Too bad the Board of Education don't give marks for pitching pennies and window breaking!"

"Every time you do a cartwheel, we lose ten yards!"

"Sergeant, this is Mr. J. Stanhope Alderson. He has money, position, many influential friends, and we can't do this to him."

"The house does wonderful on that one."

The Timid Soul

The Thrill That Comes Once in a Lifetime -:- by Webster

Life's Darkest Moment . . . BY WEBSTER

Life's Darkest Moment . . . BY WEBSTER

JOE PALOOKA

Dear mom,
When we have any time to sit around it seems we jist can't help gittin to talkin about home an you rimember all-kinds of things.

4.5

BLINKY GOLDSTEIN WAS DESCRIBIN' A CLAM-BAKE IN MAINE. YOU GOT SO HUNGRY LIS'NIN' TO 'IM---AN' THEN COLBY EVANS MAKES IT WORSE BY TELLIN' ABOUT A BARBECUE AT HIS TOWN IN NATCHEZ.

THEN A BASEBALL DISCUSHUN COMES UP. WELL YOU NEVER HEARD SUCH ARGUMUNTS. WISH I COULD'VE SEEN HONUS WAGNER WHEN HE PLAYED FER PITTSBURGH. BET POP SEEN 'IM

HARRY
DOUBLE FEATURE
SCREEMO
FREE CHINA SET
GROCERIES
AMATEUR
THEN WE GIT TO COMPARIN' THE BEST MOVIE WE EVER SEEN OR OUR FAV'RITE ACTERS--AN' YA REELIZE THAT EV'RY TOWN NO MATTER HOW SMALL HAS A MOVIE BACK HOME---

AN' RADIO--HOW YOU CAN LISSEN TO ANY-THING YOU WANT OR CHANGE THE PROGRAM--WISH WE COULD GIT LANNY ROSS RIGHT NOW---WHATTA VOICE--

AN' YOU KNOW WHY YOU'RE HERE AN' YOU'RE GLAD TO FIGHT T'KEEP DEMOCRACY AN' YOU HOPE THE FOLKS BACK HOME--EV'RY-BODY APPRISHIATES IT LIKE WE DO AN' WILL WORK AN' GIVE MORE--T'STOP THE FORCES OF EVIL---

HAM FISHER
--AN' GIVE MY LOVE TO ALL OUR LOVED ONES AN' FRIENDS--I WROTE T'STEVE AN' KNOBBY AN' HER---BLESS YOU,
JOE. XXXXXXXXXXXXXXXX

Life's Darkest Moment

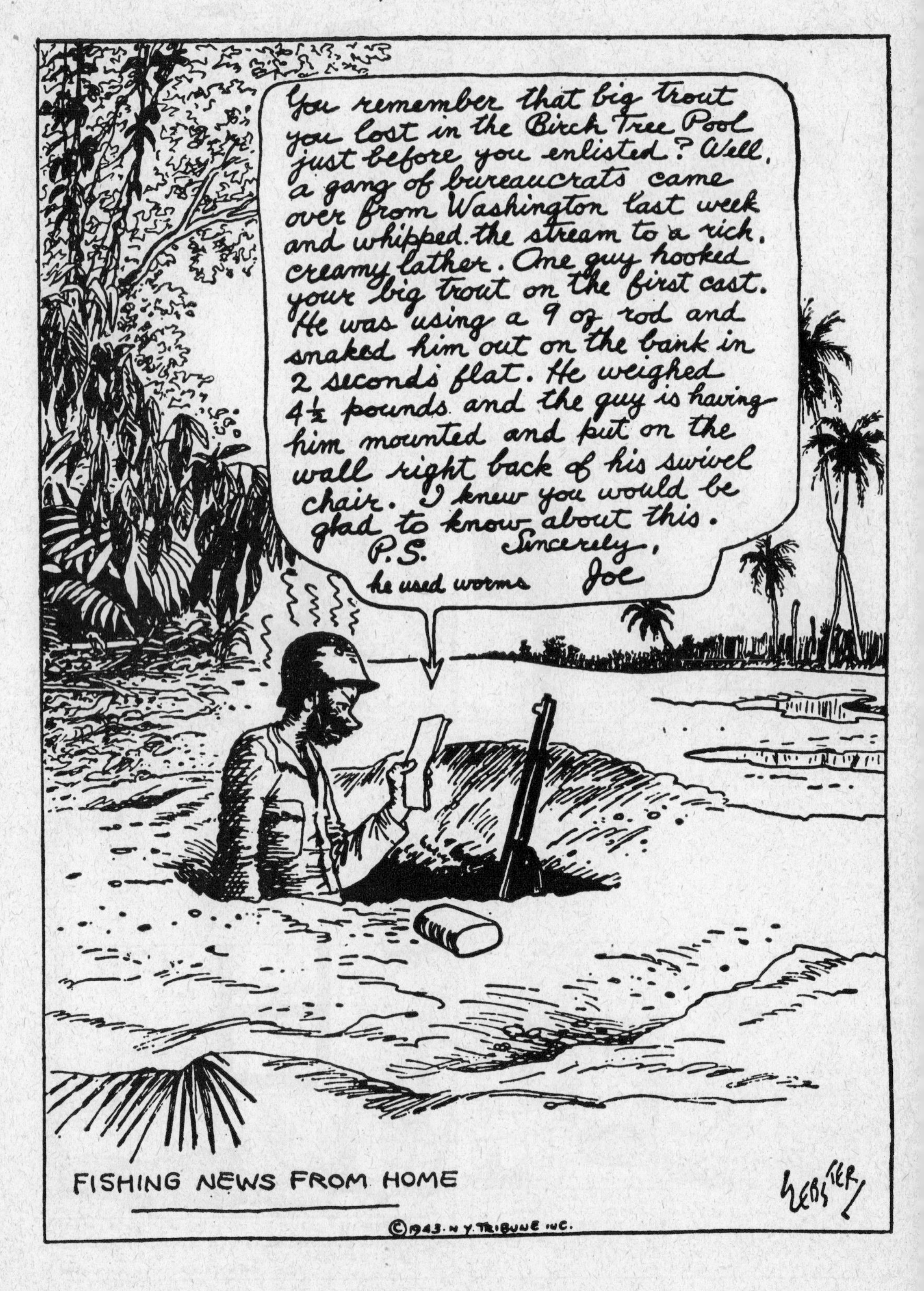

The Thrill That Comes Once in a Lifetime

THE GOOD FAIRY
AND THE ONE WISH

"Very good. And now Sergeant Wallace will acquaint you with our little list of 'Don'ts.'"

"Alfred feels that instead of doing any more work, it would be best for him to conserve all his strength to fight the Japs."

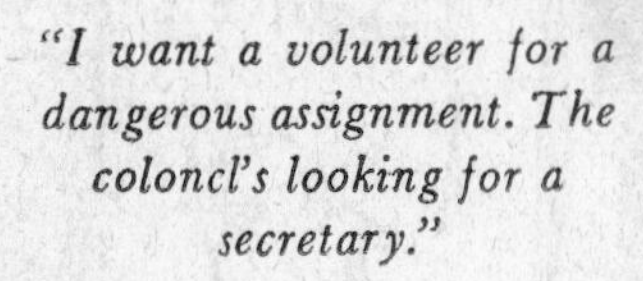

"I want a volunteer for a dangerous assignment. The colonel's looking for a secretary."

"It's a pleasure seeing you on such a grand morning, Mr. Cronin — out of golf balls?"

"Just about this time we'd be getting those American school teachers."

"Now what the hell kind of talk is that—'pierce the gloom'?"

"N-no, Smith—We don't try on skis that way!"

"Ears ain't big enuf to be one of ourn—Must belong to Lem Hawkins. I heerd him say he was short one t'other day."

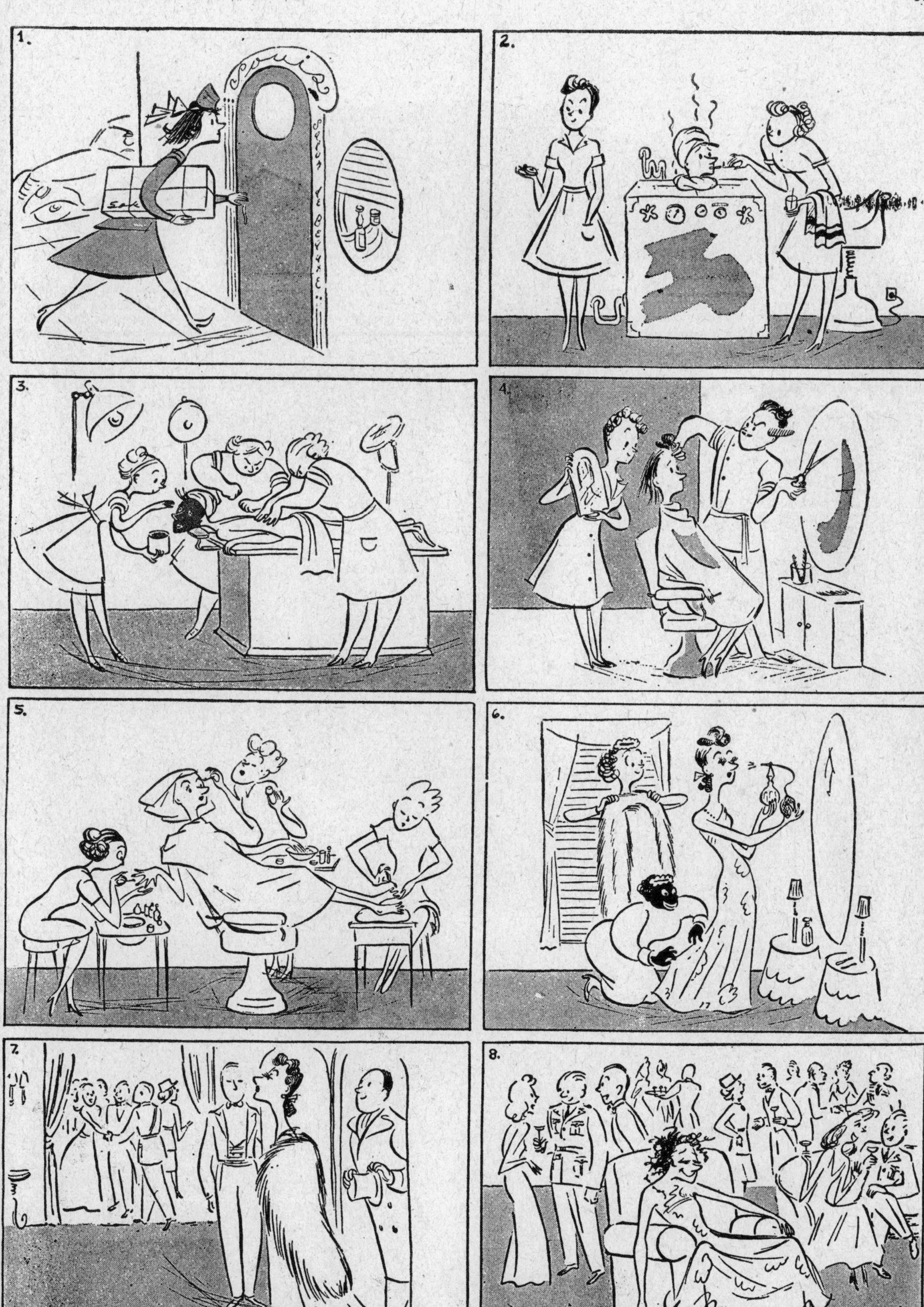
1.
2.
3.
4.
5.
6.
7.
8.
R. Macdonald

"This is your room. If you should need anything, just scream."

"Are you unhappy, darling?"
"Oh, yes, yes! Completely."

"I'm letting J.B. and R.C. fight it out themselves."

EVERYDAY MOVIES

MRS. RUMPEL'S BOARDING HOUSE

"Hm, a hot water bottle! So that's where all our hot water goes to."

GASOLINE ALLEY

EVERYDAY MOVIES

IN AND OUT OF THE RED WITH SAM

"I can't figure it out. When goods were plentiful, prices were low and business was bad. But now goods are scarce and prices are high and business is still bad!"

Ready for a Climb

"Well, it looks like a buttercup to me."

"Planning to be in Washington long, Mr. Bellew?"

"Mamma!"

"Who, me?"

"Yeah?" "Yeah!"

"Hope they send us a couple more messages by pigeon!"

GASOL

CLICK!

"Sh-h!"

"Miss Whitehead has come to tell us how to amuse sailors."

MRS. RUMPEL'S ROOMING HOUSE
"You'll get acquainted very easily here. The other roomers will start borrowing from you right away."

"Still, did you ever stop to think where you and I would be if it weren't for evil?"

"Hmmmm-Um Hmmmm—now cough, please."

"A group of sailors presented it to me."

TERRY *and the* PIRATES

Give Him the Air

"Let me know if he bothers you, ma'am."

Give Him the Air

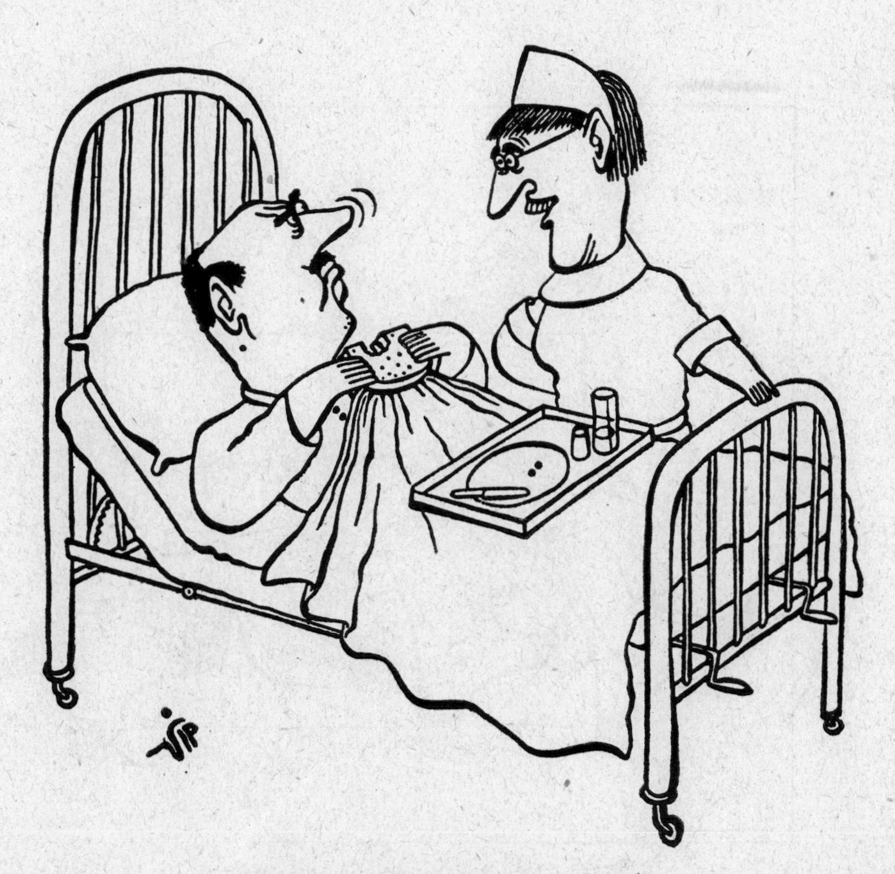

"Tastes just like old rags, doesn't it?"

TERRY *and the* PIRATES

Yankee Clipper

"Pssst—alternately, Shultz!"

TERRY *and the* PIRATES

Yankee Clipper

"I wish you'd decide on something, Butch. My feet are killing me."

TERRY *and the* PIRATES

No Rubber Shortage Here

"He's not to be disturbed on any account. And—er—I took the liberty of taking ten dollars out of his pants pocket."

Peter Arno

"... and as for those postwar trials, we can always plead insanity."

KEY TO SOURCE ABBREVIATIONS

B	*The Bellman*
BA	*Bambi* (Walt Disney)
BAY	*The Best of Art Young,* by Art Young
BCC	*Bird Center Cartoons,* by John T. McCutcheon
BM	*Ballyhoo* Magazine
BR	*Bridge,* by H. T. Webster
BS	*Between Shots,* by Percy Crosby
C	*Collier's*
CBM	*Cartoons by McCutcheon,* by John T. McCutcheon
CH	*Cartoon Humor* (Magazine)
CP	*Cincinnati Post*
D	*Dumbo* (Walt Disney)
DD	*Donald Duck* (Walt Disney)
DFN	*Don Freeman's Newsstand* (Magazine)
DMR	*Des Moines Register*
DN	New York *Daily News*
EJ	*New York Evening Journal*
FC	*Fellow Citizens,* by Gluyas Williams
FM	*Fun for the Millions,* by Carl Hauser
FMO	*For Members Only,* by Peter Arno
GB	*Golden Book*
HIA	*Hiawatta,* by Milt Gross
HT	*New York Herald Tribune*
HW	*Harper's Weekly*
J	*Judge*
JA	*New York Journal-American*
KF	*Keep 'em Flyin',* by Paul Webb
KK	*Kid Kartoons,* by Gene Carr
L	*Life*
LK	*The Little King,* by Otto Soglow
LM	*Liberty* Magazine
M	*The Masses*
MAT	*Man About Town,* by William Steig
NYA	*New York American*
NYH	*New York Herald*
NYM	New York *Daily Mirror*
NYT	*The New York Times*
OWH	*Off With Their Heads,* by Peggy Bacon
P	*Puck*
PA	*Pluto at the Zoo* (Walt Disney)
PACR	*Peter Arno's Cartoon Review*
PAH	*Peter Arno's Hullabaloo*
PAP	*Peter Arno's Parade*
PM	*PM* (Newspaper)
PP	*Pretty Pictures,* by Benjamin Travers
S	*Scribner's*
SA	*Saludos Amigos* (Walt Disney)
SEP	*The Saturday Evening Post*
SK	*Skippy,* by Percy Crosby
SLL	*Sketches of Lowly Life in a Great City,* by M. A. Woolf
SN	*Stuff and Nonsense,* by A. B. Frost
SSD	*Snow White and the Seven Dwarfs* (Walt Disney)
SW	*Squads Write!* (Collection of *Stars & Stripes* cartoons)
T	*New York Tribune*
TL	*The Liberator*
TMS	*The Mysterious Stranger and Other Cartoons,* by John T. McCutcheon
TNY	*The New Yorker Magazine*
TP	*The Pointer* (Walt Disney)
TRC	*Theodore Roosevelt in Cartoons,* by John T. McCutcheon
TS	*The Timid Soul,* by H. T. Webster
TTLP	*The Three Little Pigs* (Walt Disney)
TUD	*The Ugly Duckling* (Walt Disney)
TVS	*The Village Smithy* (Walt Disney)
VF	*Vanity Fair*
VL	*Vignettes of Life,* by J. Norman Lynd
W	*The World*
WDT	*Wasn't the Depression Terrible?* by O. Soglow
WT	*New York World-Telegram*

INDEX

F. Fox ed Nofsiger

Robt. Day Geo. Price R. TAYLOR

Shermund— CROCKETT JOHNSON Day

WINSOR McCAY vip E. Simms Campbell F. Opper

Geo. Price alain Peter Arno WEBSTER COVARRUBIAS GEO McMANUS

JOHN GROTH

...chter Davenport. Chon Day C. D. Gibson R. F. Outcault BUNNY

T. S. Allen T. E. POWERS— John Sloan Geo Be...

...RRISON · CADY ·

...cowaeHER P. L. Crosby ROLLIN KIRBY DEBECK Art Young — KING Fr...

Otterford RALPH BARTON Helen. E. Hokinson WEBSTER

John Held Jr.

R. TAYLOR Shermund— hoff

DISNEY Robt. Day Geo. Price

WINSOR McCAY vip E. Simms Campbell F. Opper C...